OOR WULLIE
& THE BROONS
TRIVIA BOOK

© DCT CONSUMER PRODUCTS (UK) LTD 2018
D.C. THOMSON AND CO. LTD,
185 FLEET STREET,
LONDON EC4A 2HS

PRINTED IN THE UK.

WULLIE'S BRAW BUCKET LOLLIES!

WHETHER THE WEATHER OF THE SCOTTISH SUMMER HAS GOT YOU DROOKIT OR ROASTIN', THESE BRAW BUCKET LOLLIES WILL HAE YE BOASTIN'!

YOU WILL NEED:
- WEE BUCKETS
- ICE LOLLY STICKS
- LEMONADE

1 POUR THE LEMONADE INTAE THE WEE BUCKETS.

BE CAREFUL NO' TAE SPILL ONY WHEN FILLIN' THE BUCKETS.

2 PUT THE BUCKETS IN THE FREEZER FOR ABOOT 20 MINUTES.

THIS WILL MAK' A BRAW WEE TREAT.

3 TAKE THEM OOT, THEN PUSH THE ICE LOLLY STICK INTAE THE MIDDLE. RETURN THEM TAE THE FREEZER TAE SET OVERNIGHT.

4 THE NEXT DAY, YE'LL HAE SOME SUPER BUCKET LOLLIES TAE COOL YE DOWN!

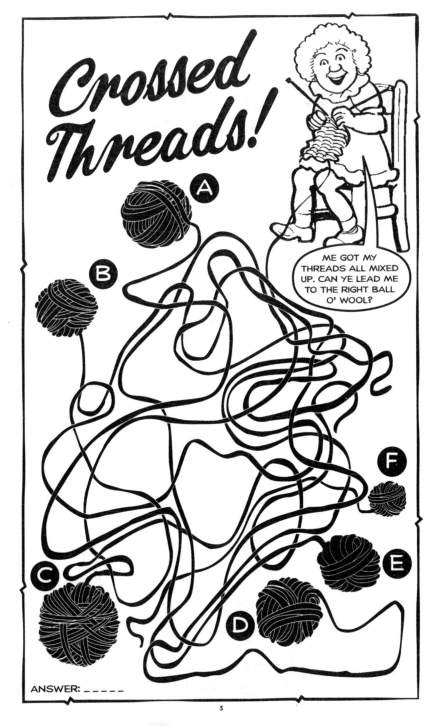

Make A Den
THE TWINS' DEN MAKING INSTRUCTIONS

WHIT YE'LL NEED: ONE TARP – MIND IT'S GUID AND WATERPROOF. BUT IF THE WEATHER'S BRAW YE CAN JIST USE A BLANKET – NO' A GIRLY ONE THOUGH. NEXT, YE'LL NEED A TOUGH LINE O' STRING. MAW'S WASHING LINE WORKS FINE.

NOO START BUILDING IT.

STEP 1:
YE MUST SCOUT THE AREA AN' BE THOROUGH! NO JAGGY STANES AND LOOSE BRANCHES HANGING ABOVE YE. BUT YE WILL NEED A COUPLE O' TREES TO SET YER DEN BETWEEN.

STEP 2:
TIE THE LINE BETWEEN TWA TREES, NO' TOO HIGH.

STEP 3:
FOLD YER BLANKET OR TARP OWER THE LINE.

STEP 4:
FINALLY, WEIGH THE BLANKET DOON WITH ROCKS SO THE BLANKET LOOKS LIKE A TRIANGLE AGAINST THE GROOND.

THERE'S NOTHING LIKE HAEING YER AIN DEN OOTSIDE TAE PLAY IN.

WE'RE JIST LIKE BEAR GRYLLS SURVIVING OOT IN THE WILDERNESS.

In It-Tae Twin It!

THE TWINS' JOKES WILL HAE YE LAUGHIN' YER BAHOOCHIE AFF!

GONE FISHIN'

JINGS! THIS MICHT BE THE CATCH O' THE DAY, BUT IT
WISNAE WHIT WULLIE WAS HOPIN' TAE FIND. CAN YOU FIND SIX
DIFFERENCES IN THE PICTURES BELOW?

Horace Broon's Scavenger Hunt

NO MATTER THE WEATHER, A SCAVENGER HUNT IS ALWAYS GOOD FUN - INSIDE OR OUT. WHETHER YOU'RE AN AMATEUR DETECTIVE OR A WANNABE EXPLORER, THERE ARE WAYS TO SUIT YOUR GAME TO EVERYONE'S TASTE AND AGE!

FIRST THING'S FIRST. YOU'VE GOT TO LAY THE GROUND-RULES!

- HOW MANY PEOPLE ARE PLAYING? YOU CAN HAVE AS LITTLE AS TWO, BUT WORKING IN TEAMS IS MORE FUN! NO SPLITTING UP! YOU'VE GOT TO WORK TOGETHER.

- HAVE A TIME LIMIT. THE SHORTER THE TIME THE MORE RUNNING AROUND AND EXCITING IT IS.

- MAKE SURE THERE IS A CLEARLY DEFINED LIMIT TO THE BOUNDARIES OF THE HUNT.

CHEEP!

WHEN SCAVENGING YOU CAN DO A NUMBER OF THINGS:

- HOW ABOUT WRITING A LIST OF ITEMS THE SCAVENGERS MUST COLLECT? (E.G. SOMETHING FLUFFY, SOMETHING GREEN, SOMETHING THAT MOVES ETC.)

IF YOU DON'T WANT TO BE CARRYING HEAVY ITEMS THEN WHY NOT MAKE IT A PHOTO SCAVENGER HUNT AND JUST TAKE PHOTOS OF THE DIFFERENT OBJECTS?

THIS IS BEST FOR PLAYING OUTSIDE AND CAN BE A FUN GAME WHILE CAMPING OR OUT WALKING.

- OR YOU COULD WRITE CLUES AND RIDDLES LEADING TO DIFFERENT LOCATIONS OR OBJECTS IN THE AREA.

WHICH IS GREAT IF IT'S RAINING AND REALLY TESTS YOUR KNOWLEDGE.

E.G. "THAR'S TASTY TREASURES IN THIS TOME" - A TASTY BOOK? WHY THAT'S MAW'S COOKBOOK!

AND LAST, BUT FOREMOST - NO CHEATING!

GOOD LUCK, SCAVENGERS!

MURDOCH'S MAD ARREST

SOMETHING BAD HAS HAPPENED IN THE
TOON O' AUCHENSHOOGLE. CAN YE HELP
P.C. MURDOCH USE THE WORD BANK TAE
REMEMBER WHIT CRIME WIS COMMITTED?

NAME..

ADDRESS...

WHAUR DAE YE BIDE ....

On this day (your name) .... wis
arrested fir (verb 1) .... the (noun)
.........................s and (verb 2) ....
the (noun) ....s in the (place noun)
.... wi' a/an (adjective) ....
(noun) .... Mrs McDonald witnessed
the heinous crime, claiming the culprit was
(adverb) .... (verb 3) ....
at the scene o' the crime, showing little tae
no remorse. I then caught the wee (noun)
.... (verb 4) .... with a/an
(adjective) .... (noun) ....
before apprehending the (adjective) ....
criminal.

10

WORD BANK

NOUNS
CHICKEN, CARROT, TOASTER, SANDWICH, GRANNY, TEACHER, COW PAT, FENCE, GIRL, BUCKET, BAIRN, SCAMP, MONKEY, HOOLIGAN, ANGEL, NURSE, HORSE, BRUSH, STICK.

PLACE NOUNS
SCHOOL, PLAYGROUND, PARK, FIELD, HIGH STREET, DOCTORS, BAKERS, FARM, FLOWER SHOW, FAIR, CIRCUS, SWIMMING POOL, POND, ZOO, CAFE, DISCO, GREEN GROCERS.

VERBS 1/2
LICKING, HUNTING, PAINTING, TRIPPING, POKING, SURROUNDING, JABBING, TICKLING, KICKING, SCARING, IRRITATING, CUDDLING, SHOVING, PETTING, SPLASHING, HASSLING.

VERB 3/4
RUNNING, DANCING, HULA-HOOPING, FLYING, BOOGIEING, HAVERING, SKIPPING, LAUGHING, BLETHERING, HOPPING, JUMPING, SINGING, LEAPING.

ADJECTIVES
FLUFFY, FILTHY, CRAZY, SHAKY, COWARDLY, SPOOKY, PINK, JUMPY, SCARED, CHEEKY, SLEEPY, MAMMOTH, SHAGGY, TERRIBLE, FLAKY, SLIPPERY, OLD, HUNGRY, PRICKLY.

ADVERBS
MERRILY, HEARTLESSLY, FLAUNTINGLY, FURIOUSLY, SNIPPILY, GENTLY, COYLY, GRACEFULLY, QUICKLY, SILENTLY, WILFULLY, CURIOUSLY, VICIOUSLY, SLOWLY, LOUDLY, EASILY.

CRACK THE CODE

WILLIAM AND HIS FRIENDS ARE AT IT AGAIN. THEY NEVER LET ME PLAY WITH THEM AND NOW THEY HAVE GONE AND INVENTED THEIR OWN LANGUAGE AND ARE COMMUNICATING VIA TIN CAN TELEPHONES! USING MY NOTES BELOW, CAN YOU PLEASE HELP ME TRANSLATE WHAT THEY ARE SAYING?

GSVHV GRM XZMH ZIV IZIV!

1 _ _ _ _ _   _ _ _   _ _ _ _   _ _ _   _ _ _ _!

ZBV, ZM' ZIV LMV PVMH DSRG DV'IV HZBRMT.

2 _ _ _, _ _'   _ _ _   _ _ _   _ _ _ _   _ _ _ _   _ _'_ _   _ _ _ _ _ _!

WZV BV GSRMP DV MVVW GSV XZMH ZM' GSV XLWV?

3 _ _   _ _   _ _ _ _ _   _ _   _ _ _ _   _ _ _   _ _ _   _ _'_,   _ _ _   _ _ _ _?

BV XZM MVEVI YV GLL XZIVUFO!

PRIMROSE'S CLUES

4 _ _   _ _ _   _ _ _ _ _   _ _   _ _ _   _ _ _ _ _ _ _!

A	B	C	D	E	F	G	H	I	J	K	L	M	N	O	P	Q	R	S	T	U	V	W	X	Y	Z
Z	Y	X	W	V	U	T	S	R	Q	P	O	N	M	L	K	J	I	H	G	F	E	D	C	B	A

12

Make Yer Ain Broons Comic!

USE THE BLANK PANELS ON THE NEXT PAGE TO WRITE AND DRAW YOUR VERY OWN BROONS COMIC STRIP!

WHO?

WHO'S GOING TO BE IN YOUR STRIP?

MAW
PAW
HEN
JOE

DAPHNE
MAGGIE
THE BAIRN
HORACE
THE TWINS
GRANPAW

HOW MANY BROONS CAN YE FIT IN A COMIC?

WHAT?

WHAT OBJECT WILL BE THE SUBJECT OF YOUR COMIC?

FALSERS!
TATTIE WINE!
TEA!
NEEPS!
CLOOTIE DUMPING!
SCALES!
BUNNET!
FISH SUPPERS!

WHERE?

WHERE'S YOUR STRIP GOING TO BE SET?

IO GLEBE STREET
THE BUS
THE BUT 'N' BEN
GLEN FESHIE
BRODIE BEACH
TONI'S CAFE
GRANPAW'S ALLOTMENT
AUCHENTOGLE FLOWER SHOW

WORDS!

SEE IF YE CAN SLIP SOME OF THESE WORDS INTO YOUR SPEECH BUBBLES!

HAUD YER WHEESHT!
BLACK AFFRONTED!
STOOSHIE!

BRAW!
MICHTY!
LADDIES!
BLETHERING!
SKINFLINT!

14

THE BROONS

Make Yer Ain Catapult

A'BODY WHO KENS ME KENS MY FAVOURITE CATTY, AN' NOO I'M HERE TAE SHOW YE HOW TAE MAKE ONE O' YER AIN!

WHIT YE'LL NEED:

- EGG CARTON
- RUBBER BANDS
- Y-SHAPED STICK
- SCISSORS

STEP 1

GO FOR A NICE WEE WALK IN THE WOODS AND LOOK AT A' THE FALLEN STICKS LYING ABOOT. TRY AN' FIND ONE THAT'S ROUGHLY Y-SHAPED (MIND YE CAN SNAP THE ENDS AFF TAE MAKE IT THE RICHT SIZE - YE WANT IT TAE BE ABOOT THE SIZE O' YER HAND).

STEP 2

SNAP A' THE LEAVES AND OTHER TWIGS AFF IT. YE CAN AYE SOAK IT IN HOT SOAPY WATER AN' PEEL A' THE BARK AFF TAE MAK' IT LOOK GUID.

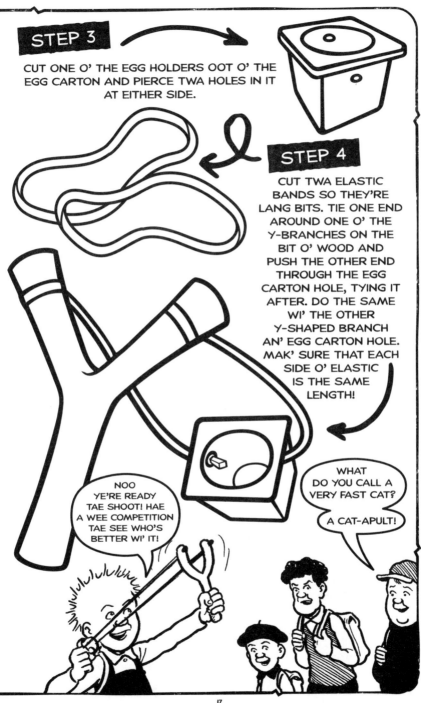

I THOUGHT YOU ONLY HAD EYES FOR ME, WILLIAM!

CRUNCH!

SORRY, PRIMROSE! JEANNIE MACLEAN WAS WULLIE'S FIRST LOVE. WULLIE TRIED TAE WIN HER AFFECTIONS IN THE 1930S.

WE'RE THE BOYS, EH, RABBIE?

ROBERT BURNS THE IMMORTAL BARD

THERE'S A BRONZE STATUE O' WULLIE IN DUNDEE CITY CENTRE. IT WAS UNVEILED AS PART O' HIS 80TH ANNIVERSARY CELEBRATIONS, AND SEES THE WEE SCUNNER AIMIN' HIS PEASHOOTER AT A STATUE O' HIS FAVOURITE POET, RABBIE BURNS.

OOR WULLIE'S HAMETOON, AUCHENSHOOGLE, GOT ITS NAME IN THE 1990S. BEFORE THEN, IT WAS KENT AS AUCHENTOGLE, WHICH IS WHAUR THE BROON FAMILY STILL BIDES TODAY.

OOR WULLIE'S HAD A LOT O' PETS OWER THE YEARS. HIS PET MOOSE, JEEMIE, STILL APPEARS IN THE STRIPS REGULARLY, AND HIS LOYAL DOG, WEE HARRY, EVEN HAS A COMIC STRIP O' HIS AIN! MA PREFERS THEM TAE THE PUDDOCKS AND RABBITS HE'S HAD.

Primrose's Scots Dictionary

> I'VE SPENT MUCH OF MY TIME STUDYING THE LANGUAGE OF WILLIAM AND HIS FRIENDS. WITH MY FINDINGS I'VE MADE A SCOTS TO ENGLISH DICTIONARY, SO YOU'LL NEVER BE STUCK AGAIN.

SCOTS	TRANSLATION
A'BODY	EVERYBODY
AULD	OLD
BAHOOCHIE	BUM
BOAB	BOB OR ROBERT
BRAW	GREAT
BREEKS	TROUSERS
BROON	BROWN
CATTY	CATAPULT
CAULD	COLD
CLAES	CLOTHES
CLARTY	DIRTY
COO	COW
CRABBIT	GRUMPY
DINNAE	DO NOT
DREICH	COLD AND WET WEATHER
DROOKIT	SOAKING WET
FITBA	FOOTBALL
FLOOER	FLOWER

SCOTS	TRANSLATION
GUID	GOOD
HAUD YER WHEESHT	BE QUIET
HAVER	TALK NONSENSE
HELP MA BOAB	GOODNESS GRACIOUS!
HOGMANAY	NEW YEAR'S EVE
JEEMIE	JAMIE
JINGS/CRIVVENS	OH MY GOODNESS
KEN	KNOW
MA	MOTHER
MESSAGES	SHOPPING
OOR	OUR
PA	FATHER
RARE	GREAT
SEMMIT	VEST
SKIVVY	SERVANT
SNAW	SNOW
WULLIE	WILLIAM
YER	YOUR

FLOOER POT

PRIMROSE'S PUZZLERS

ARE YOU READY TO TEST YOUR BRAIN AGAINST MINE? THEN IT'S TIME FOR A TRIVIA QUIZ. ALL THE QUESTIONS ARE GENERAL KNOWLEDGE AND ANY AGE CAN PLAY. ANSWERS ARE AT THE BACK - NO CHEATING!

Easy-Peasy:

1. WHAT IS THE NAME OF MICKEY MOUSE'S PET DOG?
2. HOW MANY CARDS ARE THERE IN A PACK OF CARDS?
3. IN THE FAIRYTALE OF CINDERELLA, WHAT DOES CINDERELLA LEAVE BEHIND AT THE BALL?
4. WHICH CONTINENT IS THE SAHARA DESERT LOCATED ON?
5. WHO SANG 'EVERYTHING HAS CHANGED' WITH TAYLOR SWIFT?
6. WHAT IS THE 19TH LETTER OF THE ALPHABET?
7. WHICH PLANET IS KNOWN AS THE RED PLANET?
8. TROUT, BARRACUDA AND CARP ARE ALL TYPES OF WHAT?
9. WHAT IS THE SCOTTISH WORD FOR LAKE?
10. WHICH 2016 DISNEY MOVIE FEATURES A RABBIT POLICE OFFICER CALLED JUDY HOPPS?

William Might Know:

1. WHAT'S THE LARGEST CITY IN SCOTLAND?
2. WHAT IS THE NAME OF THE HIGHEST MOUNTAIN IN AFRICA?
3. WHAT COLOURS ARE THE FIVE OLYMPIC RINGS?
4. WHAT IS THE LARGEST OCEAN?
5. HOW MANY MONTHS OF THE YEAR END WITH THE LETTER R?
6. IN WHICH COUNTRY WAS GOLF FIRST PLAYED?
7. WHICH PLUMBER HAS FEATURED IN SEVERAL POPULAR VIDEO GAMES?
8. WHICH IS THE LONGEST RIVER IN THE AMERICAS?
9. WHAT METAL IS HEAVIER - GOLD OR SILVER?
10. HOW MANY SINGLE SQUARES ARE THERE ON A CHESSBOARD?

THIS IS A BRAW GAME TAE TEST YER FRIENDS' KNOWLEDGE. THE ANSWERS ARE AT THE BACK.

HEADSCRATCHERS:

1. IN THE PHONETIC ALPHABET, WHICH CANADIAN CITY REPRESENTS THE LETTER Q?

2. WHAT IS AURORA BOREALIS COMMONLY KNOWN AS?

3. WHO PAINTED THE CEILING OF THE SISTINE CHAPEL?

4. AFTER WHICH FAMOUS PERSON WAS THE TEDDY BEAR NAMED?

5. WHICH ACRONYM DESCRIBES THE TYPE OF SLEEP ASSOCIATED WITH DREAMING?

6. WHERE DID PRESIDENT EISENHOWER OF THE UNITED STATES HAVE A RESIDENCE IN SCOTLAND?

7. WHAT ARE BABY RABBITS CALLED?

8. WHICH SHAKESPEAREAN HERO IS ALSO KNOWN AS THE PRINCE OF DENMARK?

9. WHAT IS THE CHEMICAL FORMULA FOR SNOW?

10. WHAT IS THE CAPITAL OF PERU?

PRIMROSE LEVEL
(smartie pants):

1. WHAT IS A BAWBEE: A NEW BORN GIRAFFE, A SCOTTISH COIN OF LOW VALUE OR A TRADITIONAL PIE FROM FINLAND?

2. MALLARD, SILVER APPLEYARD AND RINGED TEAL ARE ALL TYPES OF WHICH ANIMAL?

3. WHO WROTE 'THE CATCHER IN THE RYE'?

4. WHAT SHIP IS DOCKED AT OCEAN TERMINAL IN EDINBURGH?

5. IN WHAT YEAR WAS THE FIRST TELEPHONE CALL MADE?

6. WHAT DO ENTOMOLOGISTS STUDY?

7. WHO WAS THE 42ND PRESIDENT OF THE UNITED STATES?

8. WHAT IS A FATHOMETER USED TO MEASURE?

9. WHAT METAL IS USED TO GALVANISE IRON?

10. THE FILM 'RING OF BRIGHT WATER' TOLD THE STORY OF WHICH TYPE OF CREATURE?

CRACK THE CODE

THE TWINS ARE ALWAYS LITTLE SCAMPS. NOW THEY'RE SPEAKING IN CODE SO I CAN'T UNDERSTAND WHAT THEY'RE SAYING. CAN YOU HELP ME TRY TO CRACK THEIR CODE?

16,4,26,'22
11,12,7,7,8,17
23,11,8   10,24,12,7
22,26,8,8,23,12,8,22
12,17,22,12,7,8
23,11,8   5,21,8,4,7
5,12,17.

_ _ _ , _ _ _ _ _ _

_ _ _   _   _ _ _ _ _ _   _ _ _   _ _ _ _

_ _ _ _ _ _ _ _ _   _ _ _ _ _ _   _ _ _

_ _ _ _ _   _ _ _

TWINS CLUES

1	2	3	4	5	6	7	8	9	10	11	12	13	14	15	16	17	18	19	20	21	22	23	24	25	26
X	Y	Z	A	B	C	D	E	F	G	H	I	J	K	L	M	N	O	P	Q	R	S	T	U	V	W

Horace's Super Science Wordsearch

M	I	T	O	C	H	O	N	D	R	I	A	S	G	P
Q	W	E	R	T	Y	U	I	O	D	F	D	C	F	H
A	R	H	S	N	O	R	T	C	E	J	E	X	S	O
S	E	G	N	E	R	O	N	E	L	L	Z	V	Q	T
E	D	G	E	L	C	E	O	H	L	H	M	N	R	O
Q	L	H	N	E	U	T	R	S	A	Q	P	L	Z	S
N	V	E	N	E	R	G	Y	Z	S	A	H	O	U	Y
E	B	K	C	S	Q	S	T	Y	U	Y	Y	M	Z	N
U	C	V	K	T	G	H	Z	C	R	T	S	O	Q	T
R	V	D	N	U	R	S	T	V	H	G	I	P	U	H
O	B	X	P	S	S	O	O	B	B	V	C	Z	Q	E
N	O	S	A	N	S	U	N	S	A	Q	S	X	V	S
S	U	S	C	H	E	M	I	S	T	R	Y	W	X	I
T	N	E	M	I	R	E	P	X	E	A	S	S	F	S
O	S	M	O	S	I	S	Q	I	S	G	J	K	L	D

PHOTOSYNTHESIS
MITOCHONDRIA
CELLS
ENERGY
PHYSICS
CHEMISTRY
EXPERIMENT
NEURONS
ELECTRONS
OSMOSIS

CAN YOU FIND ALL 10 WORDS?

26

Make The Grade!

HORACE CANNAE BELIEVE HIS EYES! HOW COULD THE BRAINS O' THE FAMILY GET ANYTHIN' LESS THAN AN A? CAN YOU GET TOP MARKS BY FINDING ALL SIX DIFFERENCES IN THE PUZZLE BELOW?

27

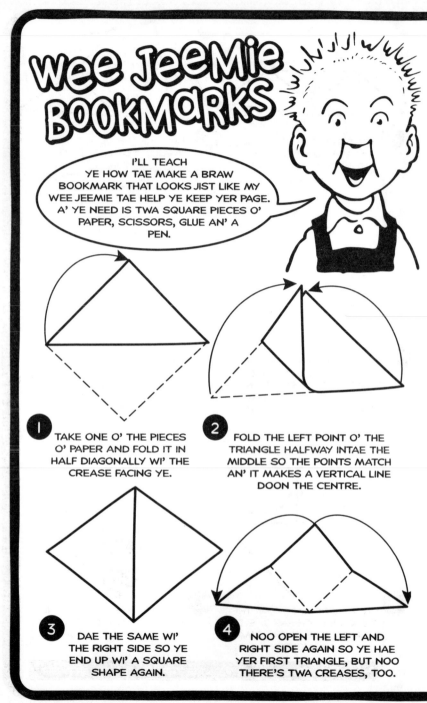

wee Jeemie Bookmarks

I'LL TEACH YE HOW TAE MAKE A BRAW BOOKMARK THAT LOOKS JIST LIKE MY WEE JEEMIE TAE HELP YE KEEP YER PAGE. A' YE NEED IS TWA SQUARE PIECES O' PAPER, SCISSORS, GLUE AN' A PEN.

1 TAKE ONE O' THE PIECES O' PAPER AND FOLD IT IN HALF DIAGONALLY WI' THE CREASE FACING YE.

2 FOLD THE LEFT POINT O' THE TRIANGLE HALFWAY INTAE THE MIDDLE SO THE POINTS MATCH AN' IT MAKES A VERTICAL LINE DOON THE CENTRE.

3 DAE THE SAME WI' THE RIGHT SIDE SO YE END UP WI' A SQUARE SHAPE AGAIN.

4 NOO OPEN THE LEFT AND RIGHT SIDE AGAIN SO YE HAE YER FIRST TRIANGLE, BUT NOO THERE'S TWA CREASES, TOO.

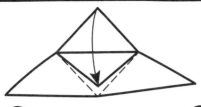

5 FOLD THE TOP TRIANGLE FLAP HALFWAY DOWN TOWARDS YE AN' THE CREASE.

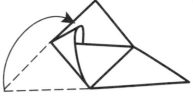

6 TAK' THE LEFT SIDE POINT AN' FOLD IT UP LIKE BEFORE, ONLY THIS TIME TUCK THE TOP HALF BEHIND THE FOLDED TRIANGLE CREASE.

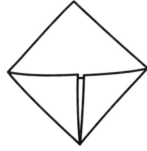

7 DAE THE SAME WI' THE RIGHT POINT SO IT MAKES A SQUARE WITH A BIG TRANGLE AT THE TOP AN' TWA SMALL TRIANGLES AT THE BOTTOM.

8 NOO, TAE MAKE IT LOOK LIKE JEEMY YE NEED TAE CUT OOT TWA CIRCLES FRAE THE OTHER PIECE O' PAPER TAE MAKE HIS EARS.

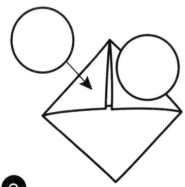

9 ONCE YE'RE HAPPY WI' THE SIZE, GLUE EACH EAR TAE THE CREASED SIDE O' THE SMALL TRIANGLES.

10 FLIP YER PAPER OVER AND DRAW ON TWA EYES AND A WEE NOSE TOO!

NOO HE'S READY TAE SLIP ONTAE THE CORNER O' YER PAGE!

Favourite Card Games

CARD GAMES ARE AYE FUN – SO LONG AS YE DINNAE HAVE TAE PAY THE WINNER. HERE'S SOME O' HEN AND JOE'S FAVOURITE GAMES FIR YE TAE TRY OOT!

GO FISH

3 OR MORE PLAYERS

EACH PLAYER IS DEALT FIVE CARDS FACE DOWN.

TAKING TURNS AND MOVING CLOCKWISE, EACH PLAYER ASKS A PERSON OF THEIR CHOICE FOR A SPECIFIC CARD RANK E.G. JACKS, FOURS, ACES. THE ASKER MUST HAVE AT LEAST ONE CARD OF THIS RANK IN THEIR OWN HAND TO ASK FOR IT.

IF THE PERSON ASKED HAS THIS CARD RANK THEY MUST HAND OVER ALL THE CARDS OF THAT RANK THEY POSSESS AND THEN THE ASKING PLAYER MAY HAVE ANOTHER TURN. BUT IF THE PLAYER DOES NOT HAVE ANY OF THAT CARD RANK THEY TELL THE ASKER TO "GO FISH" AND THE ASKER WILL TAKE THE TOP CARD FROM THE DECK.

ONCE ALL FOUR CARDS FROM THIS RANK ARE COLLECTED THEY ARE PLACED IN A PILE AND COUNT AS ONE POINT FOR THAT PLAYER. THE GAME ENDS WHEN ALL THE CARDS HAVE BEEN PLAYED.

THE WINNER IS THE PLAYER WITH THE MOST POINTS.

RUMMY

2 OR MORE PLAYERS

THE OBJECT OF THE GAME IS TO FORM MATCHED SETS CONSISTING OF GROUPS OF THREE OR FOUR OF A KIND, OR SEQUENCES OF THREE OR MORE CARDS OF THE SAME SUIT IN YOUR HAND. ACES CAN BE HIGH OR LOW.

EACH PLAYER IS DEALT SEVEN CARDS FACEDOWN.

PUT THE DECK IN THE MIDDLE AND TAKE ONE CARD FROM THE TOP AND PUT IT FACE UP NEXT TO THE PILE.

GOING CLOCKWISE, STARTING WITH THE PERSON TO THE LEFT OF THE DEALER, EACH PLAYER MAY EITHER PICK UP A CARD FROM THE TOP OF THE FACE UP PILE OR THE DECK, DEPENDING ON WHICH CARD IS DESIRED. THE PLAYER CAN EITHER KEEP OR DISCARD THE CARD THEY'VE TAKEN, SO THEY ALWAYS HAVE SEVEN CARDS IN THEIR HAND. DISCARDED CARDS ARE PLACED FACE UP ON THE PILE BESIDE THE DECK.

THE FIRST PERSON TO FORM MATCHED SETS OR A RUN WINS.

Blow Fitba

MAKE YER AIN FITBA PITCH AND PLAY THE CUP FINAL BETWEEN THE ROVERS AND UNITED - IN YER AIN HOOSE!

WHO'D HAE THOUCHT WE'D PLAY FOR ROVERS!

YOU WILL NEED:
TWO PIECES OF A4 PAPER
A RULER
BLACK FELT TIP PEN
SCISSORS
TIN FOIL
TWO STRAWS

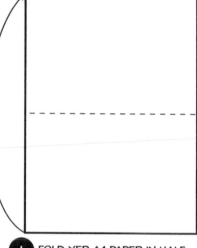

1 FOLD YER A4 PAPER IN HALF.

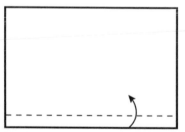

2 FOLD ABOUT 2CM OF BOTH THE OPEN SIDES OF YER HALF UPWARDS.

3 OPEN UP THE PIECE OF PAPER. USING A RULER, DRAW A RECTANGLE TO MARK YER GOALPOSTS.

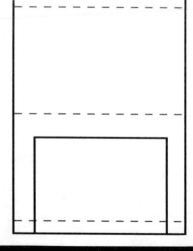

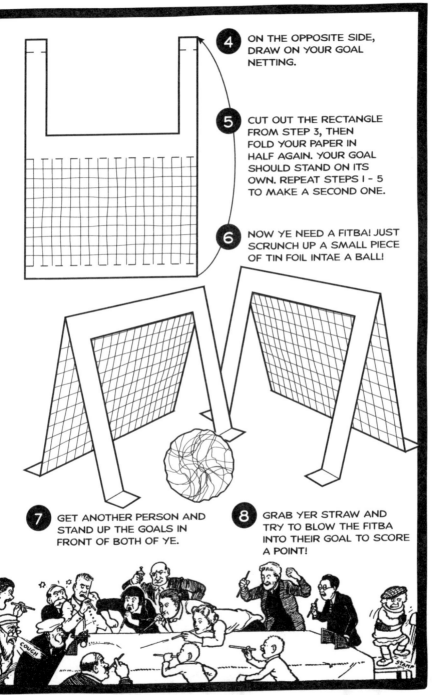

4 ON THE OPPOSITE SIDE, DRAW ON YOUR GOAL NETTING.

5 CUT OUT THE RECTANGLE FROM STEP 3, THEN FOLD YOUR PAPER IN HALF AGAIN. YOUR GOAL SHOULD STAND ON ITS OWN. REPEAT STEPS 1 - 5 TO MAKE A SECOND ONE.

6 NOW YE NEED A FITBA! JUST SCRUNCH UP A SMALL PIECE OF TIN FOIL INTAE A BALL!

7 GET ANOTHER PERSON AND STAND UP THE GOALS IN FRONT OF BOTH OF YE.

8 GRAB YER STRAW AND TRY TO BLOW THE FITBA INTO THEIR GOAL TO SCORE A POINT!

CReAtE Yer AiN Story

Yesterday mornin' (person) .... wis oot (verb) ....ing in the garden, when all of a sudden a/an (adjective) .... (noun) .... (verb) ....ed ower the fence and (verb) ....ed at him. Feart for his life (person) .... immediately (verb) ....ed away from it towards the hoose.

But the (adjective) .... (noun) .... wis too fast an' beat him tae the door. Terrified, there wis only one thing for it. (Person) .... puffed up his belly an' (verb) ....ed at the (adjective) .... (noun) .... Noo the tables had turned an' the (adjective) .... (noun) .... turned, tail between its legs and (verb) ....ed away, back o'er the fence.

(Person) .... (verb) ....ed on the spot, proud tae be such a michty hero.

WORD BANK

PERSON: WULLIE, WEE HARRY, JEEMIE, BOAB, SOAPY, ECK, PRIMROSE, GRANNY, TEACHER.

NOUNS: CAT, COO, CHICKEN, FOX, DUG, GOAT, SHEEP.

VERBS: JUMP, PLAY, LEAP, CHEER, DANCE, SPRINT, DIVE, STAGGER, FLAP, TRIP, EXPLODE, SCATTER, SWAT, JAB, BARK, SQUEAK, DONDER, SLEEP, ROAM.

ADJECTIVES: MUCKLE, GREAT, UGLY, HAIRLESS, WILD, FILTHY, FLUFFY, SLIMY, CRAZY, YAPPY, DOTTERY, CLARTY, BEARDED, MASSIVE, VERY-TACTFUL, SPLOTCHY, DROOKIT, RARE, BONNIE.

Word Jumbles

UNSCRAMBLE THESE WORD JUMBLES TO REVEAL A
WORD TAE DESCRIBE EACH O' THE BROONS SIBLINGS.

ANKLY

_ _ _ _ _

CHESISIOVUM

_ _ _ _ _ _ _ _ _ _ _

LUPPM

_ _ _ _ _

EWEBALM

_ _ _   _ _ _ _

SIBHOOK

_ _ _ _ _ _ _

CABOMNITURUS

_ _ _ _ _ _ _ _ _ _ _

EXORB

_ _ _ _ _

ALGMOOSUR

_ _ _ _ _ _ _ _ _

SLAP!

36

Maw Broons Scotch Broth

SERVES SIX TO EIGHT, BUT I DOUBLE IT WHEN I MAK' IT FOR MY LOT!

Ingredients

225g carrots (peeled an' diced)
225g neeps (peeled an' diced)
2 white onions (peeled an' diced)
1 leek sliced
100g pearl barley
100g frozen peas
10 Brussel sprouts (halved)
2.25l o' chicken or vegetable stock
1 tablespoon vegetable oil
salt and black pepper tae add tae taste

Method

1. Heat the oil in a large saucepan over a medium heat.
2. Add the chopped onion and fry, stirring continually until golden and soft.
3. Add a' the vegetables, barley and stock and heat until boiling.
4. Reduce the heat tae a simmer and cook wi' the lid on for 2-3 hours.
5. Add the peas an' cook for another fifteen minutes.
6. Season wi' salt and pepper.
7. Serve pipin' hot wi' crusty bread or oatcakes.

Maw's Marvellous Marmalade

Ingredients:

- 1.25kg Seville oranges
- 3 lemons
- 1.5kg granulated sugar
- 1 dessertspoon black treacle

Method:

1. Put a large saucepan on the hob an' fill it wi' water then bring to the boil.
2. Put a' your fruit in the water (whole) after gieing them a' a guid wash, then cover wi' a lid.
3. Bring the boil doon tae a simmer and cook for 2 hours.
4. Carefully tak' the fruit oot and put it intae an ice bath till they're cool enough tae touch.
5. Cut the fruit up and put a' the flesh intae a separate saucepan.
6. Add 1 pint o' water tae the saucepan wi' the fruit and simmer o'er a medium heat for ten minutes.
7. Strain the simmered juices through a sieve.
8. While this is strainin', slice the empty skin o' the oranges as thick or thin as ye want them.
9. Put them intae a glass bowl along wi' the strained juices frae the pulp, making sure ye get every last bit o' juice.
10. Leave this o'er night tae settle.
11. Add the juices and fruit tae a large saucepan again and bring tae the boil addin' in the sugar an' treacle.
12. Stir until all the sugar and treacle is dissolved and boil until set.
13. Pour liquid into sterile jars and allow to cool before storing in cool dry place.

Back To School Craft

NOW YOU'RE BACK AT SCHOOL, IT'S TIME TO PUT YOUR SCIENCE CAPS (GOGGLES AND LAB COATS) ON AND HAVE A GO AT MAKING SOME MAGNETIC SLIME!

WHAT YOU WILL NEED:

- 2 BOTTLES OF PVA GLUE
- LAUNDRY DETERGENT CONTAINING BORAX
- PAINT OR GLITTER FOR COLOUR

HOW TO DO IT:

1. POUR THE TWO BOTTLES OF GLUE INTO A LARGE MIXING BOWL AND ADD YOUR GLIITTER OR PAINT, STIRRING UNTIL COMPLETELY MIXED.

2. ONCE MIXED ADD THE LAUNDRY DETERGENT TO THE MIXTURE (ONLY A LITTLE AT A TIME) AND STIR UNTIL YOU'VE REACHED THE CONSISTENCY YOU WANT.

3. NOW REMOVE THE SLIME FROM THE BOWL AND KNEAD IT UNTIL IT IS READY FOR PLAY.

4. EXPERIMENT WITH DIFFERENT COLOURS AND SEE HOW MUCH SLIME YOU CAN MAKE!

MIND AND DINNAE THROW IT AT ANYONE... IT DOESNAE END WELL. TURNS OOT SOAPY ISNAE AS SLIMY AS I THOUCHT.

JUMPING PUDDOCK

MAKE YER AIN WEE JUMPING PUDDOCK OOT O' PAPER!

YE WILL NEED: A RECTANGULAR PIECE OF PAPER.

1. FOLD YER PIECE O' PAPER IN HALF VERTICALLY THEN OPEN IT OOT. NEXT FOLD THE TOP CORNERS DOON TOWARDS THE OPPOSITE SIDE O' THE PAPER THEN UNFOLD. YER CREASES SHOULD MAKE AN X-SHAPE.

2. FOLD THE PAPER ALONG THE MIDDLE O' THE X TAE MAKE ANOTHER CREASE.

3. HOLD THE PAPER AT THE SIDES, BRING THE POINTS DOWN TAE THE CENTRE LINE, THEN FLATTEN TAE CREATE A TRIANGLE.

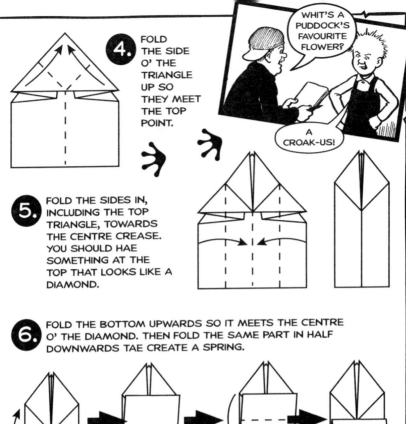

4. FOLD THE SIDE O' THE TRIANGLE UP SO THEY MEET THE TOP POINT.

WHIT'S A PUDDOCK'S FAVOURITE FLOWER?

A CROAK-US!

5. FOLD THE SIDES IN, INCLUDING THE TOP TRIANGLE, TOWARDS THE CENTRE CREASE. YOU SHOULD HAE SOMETHING AT THE TOP THAT LOOKS LIKE A DIAMOND.

6. FOLD THE BOTTOM UPWARDS SO IT MEETS THE CENTRE O' THE DIAMOND. THEN FOLD THE SAME PART IN HALF DOWNWARDS TAE CREATE A SPRING.

7. TURN IT OVER AND YER JUMPING PUDDOCK IS DONE! TAE GET HIM TAE HOP JUST PRESS YER FINGER ON HIS BAHOOCHIE AND LET GO!

I LIKE TAE DRAW WEE FACES ON MINE. THE SMALLER YER PIECE O' PAPER THE FURTHER YER PUDDOCK WILL JUMP!

Outdoor Games

TRY OOT THESE OOTDOOR GAMES WE LIKE TAE PLAY!

ROBIN HOOD VS THE SHERIFF O' NOTTINGHAM!

ONE TEAM IS ROBIN HOOD AND HIS MERRY MEN, AND THE OTHER TEAM IS THE SHERIFF O' NOTTINGHAM AND HIS POLIS! THE MERRY MEN HAE TAE HIDE AND THE POLIS HAVE TAE FIND THEM!

GRANPAW'S FOOTSTEPS!

THIS IS A BRAW GAME TAE PLAY. THE PERSON WHO IS GRANPAW STANDS FACING A WALL, THE OTHER PLAYERS HAVE TAE TAKE IT IN TURNS TAE SNEEK UP AND TAP HIM ON THE SHOULDER. BUT IF HE TURNS ROOND AND CATCHES YE MOVING – YE'RE OOT!

CAPTURE THE FLAG!

SPLIT INTAE TWO TEAMS – BLUE AND RED. TUCK A HANDKERCHIEF THE COLOUR O' YER TEAM INTO YER TROOSERS AND TRY TAE GET THE OTHER TEAM'S HANDKERCHIEFS WITHOOT THEM GETTING YOURS FIRST!

CONKERS CONQUERORS

EVERTHING YE NEED TAE KNOW FOR PLAYING CONKERS!

WHAT YE'LL NEED:

- THE BEST CONKERS YE CAN FIND FRAE A HORSE CHESTNUT TREE
- A PIECE O' STRING, ABOOT 25-30 CM LONG
- PALS TAE PLAY WI' YE

WHIT TAE DO:

- GET YER CHOSEN CONKER AND ASK AN ADULT TO CAREFULLY PIERCE A HOLE THROUGH THE MIDDLE O' IT.

- NOO THREAD YER STING THROUGH THE HOLE AND PULL THE CONKER TAE THE BOTTOM, THEN TIE THE ENDS SO THE CONKER DISNAE FALL AFF.

- MAKE AS MANY AS YE LIKE SO THE GAME CAN LAST AS LONG AS POSSIBLE.

- TAK' IT IN TURNS TAE HIT YER OPPONENT'S CONKER.

- IF IT'S YER TURN, PULL BACK THE STRING AN TAK' AIM THEN LET IT GO.

- IF IT'S YER OPPONENT'S TURN YE MUST HOLD YER CONKER STILL.

- KEEP DAEING THIS TILL ONE O' THEM SMASHES. THE WINNER GETS A POINT.

- KEEP PLAYIN' TILL YE'VE RUN OOT O' CONKERS AN' HAE A WINNER!

IF YE WANT TAE MAKE YER CONKERS HARDER SOAK THEM IN VINEGAR AN' BAKE THEM IN THE OVEN! IF YE WANT A REALLY GUID ONE THEN SAVE IT FOR NEXT YEAR - THE AULDER THE BETTER!

WULLIE'S CAMPING TIPS

WHIT TAE BRING!

- A TENT (MAKE SURE IT'S BIG ENOUGH FOR YE)
- A SLEEPING BAG
- A SLEEPING MAT
- FIRST AID KIT
- WATER AND FOOD BOWLS (FOR WEE HARRY)
- PLASTIC PLATES AND UTENSILS
- FOOD! TINS AND CANS O' FOOD ARE BEST - MIND AND RECYCLE THEM EFTER
- WET WIPES (FOR CAMPING 'SHOWERS'!)
- WATERPROOFS - EVEN IN SUMMER
- AND MOST IMPORTANT O' ALL... TOILET PAPER

WHERE TAE CAMP!

- IF YE'RE CAMPING IN THE WOODS, PITCH YER TENT UNDER LIVE TREES (MAKE SURE THEY'VE GOT GREEN LEAVES GROWING FRAE THEM) NO ROTTING ONES, IN CASE THEY FALL ON YE!

- IF IT'S MARSHY THEN YE'LL WANT TAE PITCH UP ON HIGHER GROUND AWAY FROM THE WATER.

- IF YER HIGH UP, THEN PITCH BY ROCKS AND TREES TAE SHELTER YE FROM THE WIND - MIND AND MAKE SURE IT'S NO' THE ONLY TREE THOUGH, AS IT MICHT ATTRACT LIGHTNING.

- AND MOST IMPORTANT - MIND AND TRY PITCHIN' YER TENT AT HAME BEFORE YE GO. YE DINNAE WANT TO GET THERE AND REALISE YE CANNAE DAE IT...

BEST KNOTS TAE KEN!

OVERHAND KNOT

MAKE A LOOP WI' YER ROPE.

THEN TWIST BOTH ENDS AND PASS 'EM BACK THROUGH THE LOOP IN THE OPPOSITE DIRECTION AND PULL TILL TAUT.

HALF HITCH

THIS IS FOR TYING ROOND SOMETHIN' LIKE A POLE OR BRANCH.

LOOP THE ROPE AROUND THE OBJECT SO ONE END IS ON EITHER SIDE.

THEN TAK' THE RIGHT END O' THE ROPE AND TWIST IT ROOND THE LEFT SIDE O' THE ROPE MAKING A LOOP WHICH YE PULL THE ROPE THROUGH.

CAMPING GAMES!

TWENTY QUESTIONS

NOMINATE A PERSON TAE THINK O' A SUBJECT OR OBJECT. THIS PERSON IS THEN THE SPEAKER. NOO THE REST O' THE PLAYERS WILL TAK' IT IN TURNS TAE ASK THE SPEAKER YES OR NO QUESTIONS ABOUT THE SUBJECT/OBJECT, TRYING TAE FIGURE OOT WHIT IT IS. IF YE MANAGE TAE GUESS WHIT IT IS WITHIN TWENTY QUESTIONS, THEN YE WIN AN' IT'S YER TURN TAE BE THE SPEAKER. IF NO', THEN THE SPEAKER WINS AND GETS ANITHER SHOT!

MAKE ME LAUGH

TAK' TURNS SITTING IN THE HOT SEAT WI' EVERYONE ELSE TRYING TO MAKE YE LAUGH – IF YE SHOW YER TEETH, YE'RE OOT!

ONCE YE'VE HAD A GOOD LAUGH IT'S TIME TAE TELL SOME SPOOKY STORIES...

Silly Sookers

GRANPAW BROON'S A FAN O' THE GREAT OOTDOORS. IT'S THE ONLY PLACE HE GETS PEACE TAE EAT HIS SWEETS! CAN YE SPOT 6 DIFFERENCES IN THE PICTURES BELOW?

BONNY SCOTLAND

IT'S BRAW TAE GO OOTSIDE! FILL IN THIS CROSSWORD AND SEE HOW MUCH YE KEN ABOOT ME AND THE BONNY LAND O' SCOTLAND!

ACROSS

2. WHAT PURPLE FLOWERS GROW IN THE HIGHLANDS?

3. WHAT'S THE SCOTS WORD FOR LAKE?

5. WHAT IS THE CAPITAL OF SCOTLAND?

7. WHAT DOES WULLIE CALL THE AMPHIBIANS HE CATCHES?

8. WHAT THE NAME OF THE BURN WHERE WULLIE LIKES TO FISH?

10. WHOSE GARDEN DOES WULLIE STEAL APPLES FROM?

11. WHAT'S SCOTLAND'S LONGEST RIVER?

12. WHAT IS WULLIE'S FAVOURITE HEARTY SCOTTISH BREAKFAST?

DOWN

1. WHAT'S THE HIGHEST POINT IN SCOTLAND?

4. WHAT SHAGGY, HORNED ANIMALS DON'T MIND THE SCOTTISH COLD?

6. WHERE DOES WULLIE LIKE TO RACE HIS CARTIE?

9. WHAT DO YOU CALL A MOUNTAIN WHICH IS OVER 3,000 FEET HIGH?

49

PA'S GUIDE TAE GARDENING

THERE'S NOTHING BETTER THAN RELAXING IN YER AIN GARDEN - ESPECIALLY WHEN WULLIE'S NO' CAUSING ANY MISCHIEF. I'VE SPENT MANY YEARS IN MINE, AN' I'VE A FEW GUID TIPS FOR KEEPING IT LOOKING BRAW.

● FIRST AND FOREMOST - GET YOURSELF A COMPOST HEAP FOR A' YER FOOD WASTE - NAE MEAT (UNLESS YOU WANT RATS!). COMPOST HEAPS ARE BRAW TAE USE FOR GROWING NEW PLANTS.

● SAVE A' YOUR USED TEABAGS. LIKE YER COMPOST, TEABAGS ARE GUID PLANT FOOD AN' WILL HELP NEW PLANTS GROW - IT ESPECIALLY GIVES ROSES A REAL BOOST.

● YE DINNAE HAE TAE BE TOO TIDY WI' YOUR GARDEN. LEAVING A CORNER TAE GROW WILD MAKES A GOOD ECOSYSTEM FOR WILDLIFE AND YE MIGHT FIND YERSELF A GUID WEE SPOT FOR BIRDWATCHING.

● IF YE'RE LIKE ME AND YOU FIND BENDING OVER ALL THE TIME MAKES YE SORE, THEN YE CAN BUILD A RAISED BED. THIS IS GUID IF YE'VE A WEE GARDEN TOO AS YE CAN GROW MORE IN THIS SPACE.

NOW, WE HAVE TO TALK ABOOT WEEDS - AYE, IT'S NO' ALWAYS ROSY IN THE GARDEN - HA-HA!

● YE'VE GOT TAE KNOW YER WEEDS - THERE ARE TWO TYPES: ANNUAL AND PERENNIAL. ANNUAL WEEDS ARE THE EASIEST TAE DEAL WITH. THEY GROW AND DIE OFF WITHIN ONE SEASON. PERENNIALS RETURN YEAR AFTER YEAR.

● THE BEST WAY O' DEALING WITH WEEDS IS TAE NO' DISTURB THE SOIL TOO MUCH - DIG ONLY WHERE YOU NEED TAE AND IF YE DAE, PLANT SOMETHING THERE OR COVER IT WITH WOODCHIP OR STONES.

● DAE ALL YER WEEDING AFTER IT RAINS. IT SHOULDNAE BE HARD WAITING FOR IT TAE RAIN IN SCOTLAND, BUT ONCE IT HAS, THE SOIL IS AYE LOOSER SO IT'S EASIER TAE PULL THE WEEDS OOT.

● IF YE'VE LOTS O' WEEDS IN ONE AREA, COVER THEM WITH BLACK TARP FOR A FEW WEEKS. THIS'LL BLOCK OOT THE LIGHT AND THEY'LL SOON SHRIVEL UP.

● WEEDS GROWING IN CRACKS CAN BE THE WORST AS THEY'RE HARD TAE REACH. BUT IF YE POUR BOILING WATER OVER THEM, THIS WILL KILL THE WEEDS, MAKING THEM EASIER TAE PULL OOT.

Granpaw's Better Guide Tae Gardening

A GREENHOOSE IS GUID FIR STRETCHING SEASONS AND GROWING PLANTS THAT NEED MAIR WARMTH AN' SHELTER. HERE'S SOME TIPS TAE GETTIN' THE MOST O' YOURS!

● NOO, WE A' KEN GREENHOOSES CAN BE OWER EXPENSIVE, BUT YE'D BE SURPRISED HOW MANY FOLK ARE TRYING TAE SELL THEIRS. CHECK OOT THE LOCAL PAPERS, ADS IN YER POST OFFICE AND EVEN ONLINE FOR FOLK NEARBY WHO ARE WANTING TAE SELL THEIRS.

● ONCE YE'VE GOT YER GREENHOOSE, ITS IMPORTANT TAE FIND THE BEST SPOT FOR IT. YE WANT AS MUCH SUN AS POSSIBLE SO CHECK WHICH SPOTS GET THE MOST - FOR THE LONGEST! REMEMBER, AN EAST FACING GREENHOOSE'LL ONLY GET SUN IN THE MORNING. AN' MAKE SURE THERE'S NAE TREES OR BUILDINGS BLOCKING ITS LIGHT IF POSSIBLE.

● A GUID GREENHOUSE IS LIKE A GUID RELATIONSHIP - YE NEED TAE HAE GOOD, FIRM FOUNDATIONS. YE DINNAE WANT YER GREENHOOSE GETTING DAMAMGED OR FALLIN' DOON ON YER NICE PLANTS. ALSO, I KEN WOOD LOOKS BRAW, BUT IT'LL ROT IN THE RAIN (AN' THERE'S PLENTY O' THAT). YER BEST BET IS A GUID ALUMINIUM FRAME - YE CAN EVEN PAINT IT IF YE FANCY. HIGH EAVES MEAN HEN WINNAE BANG HIS HEID, TOO!

● IF YE'RE BUILDING ON SOIL THEN YE CAN JIST GROW STRAIGHT FRAE THAT, BUT IF YE'VE GOT SLABS OR CONCRETE THEN JIST USE POTS OR GROWBAGS. RAISED BEDS AND SHELVING GIES YE MORE SPACE TAE, SO INVEST IF YE CAN.

● IF YER GREENHOOSE IS BUILT FAR AWA' FRAE YER HOOSE OR HOSE YE CAN CREATE YER AIN NEARBY STORAGE. ALL YE NEED IS A PLASTIC TUBE, ABOOT 2 METRES LONG AN' 5CM THICK, AN' A WATER BUTT. SIMPLY CONNECT THE PLASTIC TUBE TAE THE DRAINPIPE ON YER GREENHOOSE AND HAE THE OTHER END INSIDE YER WATER BUTT. WHEN IT RAINS (AN' IT WILL, OFTEN) THE WATER'LL COLLECT IN THE DRAINPIPE AND DRAIN INTAE THE WATER BUTT VIA THE TUBE, SO YE WINNAE HAE TAE CARRY A HEAVY WATERING CAN OWER FAR.

MUD PIE RECIPE

METHOD:

- MELT THE BUTTER IN A SAUCEPAN OVER A LOW HEAT
- REMOVE THE BUTTER FROM THE HEAT ONCE MELTED AND STIR IN THE SUGAR AND COCOA
- ADD THE DRIED FRUIT AND ANY OTHER ADDITIONAL FILLINGS YOU DESIRE AND MIX
- LINE A CAKE TIN WITH BAKING PARCHMENT AND POUR IN THE TASTY MIX
- NOW PRESS DOWN ON THE MIXTURE UNTIL IT IS SOLID AND LEAVE TO COOL IN A FRIDGE FOR A MINIMUM OF TWO HOURS
- (LICK THE BOWL AND SPOON)
- BOIL WATER IN A PAN AND PLACE CHOCOLATE IN A BOWL ABOVE IT, STIR CONTINUOUSLY UNTIL MELTED AND SMOOTH
- REMOVE THE CAKE TIN FROM THE FRIDGE AND EMPTY THE BISCUIT MIXTURE (WHICH SHOULD BE SOLID NOW) ONTO A PLATE
- POUR OVER THE MELTED CHOCOLATE AND SMOOTH WITH A PALLET KNIFE (ADD ANY ADDITIONAL TOPPINGS)
- CUT YOURSELF A SLICE AND EAT WITH A CUP OF TEA!

WE'RE LUCKY TAE HAE A PAL LIKE PRIMROSE. WHIT A FEED!

AYE, SHE'S AN AWFY BRAW BAKER.

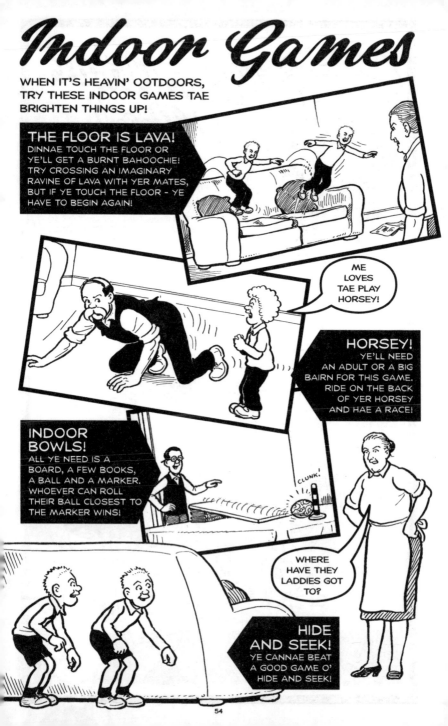

55

I Ken What I Ken!

1. HOW MANY TIDDLERS
HAVE THE BAIRNS
CAUGHT?
A. THREE
B. ONE
C. TWO

2. WHOSE CUP IS MAW
POURING TEA INTAE?
A. GRANPAW
B. MAGGIE
C. DAPHNE

3. HOW MANY SANDWICHES
ARE IN THE PICTURE
A. FOUR
B. SIX
C. EIGHT

4. WHAT IS HEN DRINKING?
A. GINGER BEER
B. FIZZY MILK
C. LEMONADE

5. HOW MANY BROONS
ARE WEARING HATS?
A. THREE
B. FOUR
C. FIVE

6. WHO IS PLAYING MUSIC
ON THE RECORD PLAYER?
A. HORACE
B. DAPHNE
C. JOE

I GOT FIVE OUTTA SIX RIGHT! TOLD YOU I'M NO' SENILE!

Match The Word Tae The Image

ISN'T IT BRAW HAEING THE FAMILY A' TOGETHER! BUT IN SUCH A COSY SCENE, HOW MANY OF THESE SCOTTISH THINGS CAN YE FIND?

- ☐ BREEK(S)
- ☐ BAHOOCHIE(S)
- ☐ BUNNET(S)
- ☐ DRAM(S)
- ☐ HAGGIS
- ☐ LUG(S)
- ☐ NEB(S)
- ☐ OXTER(S)

WULLIE'S pranks!

I LOVE TAE PLAY A TRICK OR PRANK - HERE ARE SOME O' MINE YE COULD TRY OOT YERSELF!

BUCKETHEID

THIS PRANK IS A CLASSIC. ASK AN ADULT TAE HELP YE PUT A BUCKET O' WATER ON AN OPEN DOOR, THEN WHEN SOMEONE COMES THROUGH THEY'LL GET DROOKIT!

MASH TATTIE SUNDAE

REPLACE THE ICE CREAM WITH MASH TATTIES - IT LOOKS REALLY BRAW BUT THEY'LL GET A SHOCK WHEN THEY REALISE IT ISNAE ICE CREAM!

PUDDOCK IN A BOX

HIDE A HOPPING PUDDOCK TOY IN A BOX THEN GIVE IT TO YER VICTIM. THE PUDDOCK WILL HOP OOT AND GIE THEM A JOLT!

Welcome To 10 Glebe Street!

IT'S WHERE THE BROONS LAY THEIR HATS BUT HOW MUCH DO YE KEN ABOUT 10 GLEBE STREET?

GLEBE STREET

ACROSS

3. WHAT DO THE BROONS CALL THE CHIMNEY STACK IN 10 GLEBE STREET? (3)

5. WHICH BROON HATES THE BATHROOM SCALES? (6)

6. WHAT'S THE NAME OF THE BAIRN'S FAVOURITE TOY? (5)

7. WHICH BROON IS TOO TALL FOR THEIR BED? (3)

8. WHAT KIND OF TRADITIONAL SCOTTISH DESSERT IS THE BROONS' FAVOURITE? (7,8)

9. WHO DOES MOST OF THE COOKING IN THE HOUSE? (3,5)

11. HOW MANY BROONS LIVE AT 10 GLEBE STREET? (3)

12. WHAT USUALLY BRINGS ALL THE BROONS TOGETHER? (6,4)

DOWN

1. WHAT TOWN IS 10 GLEBE STREET IN? (11)

2. WHICH BROON SPENDS THE MOST TIME IN THE BATHROOM? (6)

4. WHERE DOES GRANPAW BROON SPEND MOST OF HIS TIME? (9)

10. WHO DOES HEN SHARE A ROOM WITH? (3)

Rainy Day Activities

LIVING IN SCOTLAND, IT'S AYE RAINING, BUT I'VE FIGURED OOT WAYS TAE AMUSE MYSELF EVEN ON THE DREICHEST O' DAYS.

SOME O' MY FAVOURITE THINGS TAE DAE INSIDE ARE HAEIN' A TREASURE HUNT AN' LEAVING CLUES AROUND THE HOOSE FIR SOMEONE TAE FIND THEN HAEIN' A WEE PRIZE AT THE END. ANOTHER GUID ONE IS HIDE AN' SEEK, MAKIN' A DEN OOT O' PILLOWS, BUT MA DISNAE REALLY LIKE THAT...

BOARD GAMES ARE GUID TAE, BUT TAE BE HONEST I WIS BORED O' BOARD GAMES – UNTIL I INVENTED MY AIN! SO IF YE'RE SICK O' YER AIN ONES TOO, YE CAN HAE A WEE SHOT O' THE ONE I MADE ON THE NEXT PAGE.

FEELIN' INSPIRED? WHY DON'T YE HAE A GO AT MAKING YER AIN BORED GAME? A' YE NEED IS A BIG PIECE O' PAPER, SOME PENCILS – MIND AND MAKE IT COLOURFUL, DICE AN' PLAYER PIECES THEN MAKE UP YER AIN RULES (TRY AN' MAKE 'EM AS DAFT AS POSSIBLE!).

HOW ABOOT:

● A'BODY HAS TAE TALK LIKE A PIRATE OR MISS THEIR TURN.

● IF YE LAND ON THE SAME SQUARE AS SOMEONE ELSE YE HAVE TAE THUMB WAR FOR THE SPOT AN' THE LOSER HAS TAE MOVE BACK 4 SPACES.

● IF YE CALL SOMEONE BY THEIR FIRST NAME, THEN YE'VE TAE MISS A TURN (IT'S HARDER THAN YE THINK!).

● ALL PLAYERS MUST SAY "MEOW" INSTEAD OF "NOW" – IF THEY DINNAE THEN THEY HAVE TAE DO A DARE.

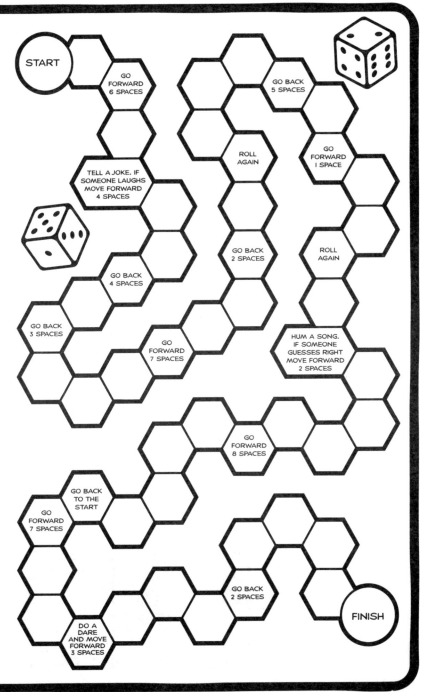

START

GO FORWARD 6 SPACES

GO BACK 5 SPACES

TELL A JOKE. IF SOMEONE LAUGHS MOVE FORWARD 4 SPACES

ROLL AGAIN

GO FORWARD 1 SPACE

GO BACK 4 SPACES

GO BACK 2 SPACES

ROLL AGAIN

GO BACK 3 SPACES

GO FORWARD 7 SPACES

HUM A SONG. IF SOMEONE GUESSES RIGHT MOVE FORWARD 2 SPACES

GO FORWARD 8 SPACES

GO BACK TO THE START

GO FORWARD 7 SPACES

GO BACK 2 SPACES

DO A DARE AND MOVE FORWARD 3 SPACES

FINISH

Maw Broon's Family Recipe

NOO FOR A CLASSIC FAMILY RECIPE THAT'LL KEEP A'BODY HAPPY!

MAW BROON'S FAMOUS MINCE, TATTIES AND DOUGHBALLS

SERVES 10

INGREDIENTS

FIR THE MINCE:
1 KG STEAK MINCE
4 ONIONS DICED
4 CARROTS DICED
1 NEEP DICED (OPTIONAL)
BEEF STOCK
100G FROZEN GARDEN PEAS
1 TSP WHOLEGRAIN MUSTARD
1 TBS WORCESTERSHIRE SAUCE
1 TBS VEGETABLE OIL

FIR THE TATTIES:
6-8 POTATOES PEELED AND DICED
BUTTER
MILK

FIR THE DOUGH BALLS:
10 TBS SELF-RAISING FLOUR
5 TBS SUET
SALT
WATER

OI!

64

METHOD:

1. WARM A TABLESPOON OF OIL OVER A MEDIUM HEAT IN A LARGE SAUCEPAN.

2. BROWN THE MINCE FOR 2 MINUTES THEN ADD THE ONIONS, MUSTARD AND SEASON WI' SALT AND PEPPER.

3. COVER THE MINCE WI' BEEF STOCK AND ADD YER CARROTS, GARDEN PEAS, NEEPS IF YE'RE HAEING THEM, MUSTARD AND WORCESTERSHIRE SAUCE THEN LEAVE TO SIMMER.

4. PUT THE TATTIES INTAE A LARGE SAUCE PAN AND COVER WI' WATER, BRINGING IT TAE THE BOIL. LEAVE FIR 20 MINUTES.

5. MEANWHILE, MIX FLOUR, A PINCH OF SALT AND SUET TOGETHER, ADDING DROPS OF WATER UNTIL THE MIXTURE IS THICK BUT STICKY.

6. COAT YER HANDS IN FLOUR AND ROLL THE DOUGH INTAE TEN BALLS.

7. PLACE DOUGHBALLS INTAE THE MINCE WHILE IT'S SIMMERING AND COVER WI' THE LID FIR 15 MINUTES.

8. WHEN THE TATTIES ARE NICE AN' TENDER, DRAIN, THEN MASH WI' BUTTER, MILK AND SEASON WI' SALT AN' PEPPER.

9. PLATE UP AND CALL THE FAMILY BEN!

Make Yer Ain Oor Wullie Comic!

USE THE BLANK PANELS ON THE NEXT PAGE TAE WRITE AND DRAW YER VERY AIN OOR WULLIE COMIC STRIP!

WHO?

WHO'S GOIN' TAE BE IN YER STRIP?

WULLIE!

BOAB!

SOAPY SOUTAR!

WEE ECK!

PRIMROSE!

MA!

PA!

PC MURDOCH!

DINNAE FORGET ABOOT MY BUCKET!

WHERE?

WHERE'S YER STRIP GOIN' TO BE SET?

FARMER GREY'S FARM!

WULLIE'S HOOSE!

STOORIE BURN!

WULLIE'S SHED!

SCHOOL!

GRUMPY GREEN'S GARDEN!

TONI'S CAFE!

STOORIE BRAE!

WHAT?

WHAT OBJECT WILL BE THE SUBJECT O' YER COMIC?

AIPPLES!

CARTIE!

BAFFIES!

JEEMIE!

WHOOPEE CUSHION!

WATER PISTOL!

CATAPULT!

PC MURDOCH'S HAT!

WORDS!

SEE IF YE CAN SLIP SOME O' THESE WORDS INTAE YER SPEECH BUBBLES!

CRIVVENS!

HELP MA BOAB!

DROOKIT!

JINGS!

BAHOOCHIE!

AWFY!

CLARTY!

SCUNNER!

OOR WULLIE

Maw Broon's Crafty Wordsearch

WHIRRRR!

DO YE THINK YE'RE AS CANNY AS MAW BROON IS CRAFTY? WHY NO' TRY AN' FIND A' THE CRAFT WORDS YE CAN IN OOR WORDSEARCH!

D	C	H	Y	Q	M	A	C	R	A	M	E	T	X	E
V	G	B	C	A	V	N	S	V	F	B	B	Z	M	H
N	D	Y	I	T	K	N	I	T	T	I	N	G	Y	C
G	N	I	T	N	I	A	P	R	E	G	N	I	F	A
I	C	A	J	J	P	T	Y	A	K	O	T	C	P	M
Y	R	E	T	T	O	P	S	O	T	E	J	J	W	R
N	O	F	D	L	P	J	O	S	A	T	C	Q	X	E
O	C	Y	A	A	Q	B	G	C	S	S	E	H	T	I
B	H	H	S	M	P	I	O	R	P	O	V	R	Q	P
B	E	L	G	A	N	S	Y	N	F	N	R	B	N	A
I	T	A	R	N	Y	V	O	D	Y	N	C	C	C	P
R	Y	C	E	V	I	T	E	M	W	K	Q	S	P	E
Q	S	W	S	J	T	W	M	O	S	A	I	C	W	B
R	A	L	C	U	Z	H	E	F	E	Q	V	Q	G	V
L	L	A	B	C	E	Y	T	S	N	E	E	D	L	E

KNITTING
PATTERN
CROSS-STITCH
CROCHET
SEWING

SCRAPBOOK
FINGER PAINTING
PAPIER MACHE
RIBBON
BUTTON

TEA COSY
POTTERY
MOSAIC
MACRAME
NEEDLE

How Tae Make A Paper Plane

FOLLOW OOR INSTRUCTIONS AND YE'LL HAE A PAPER PLANE TAE LOB AT HORACE LIKE WE DAE!

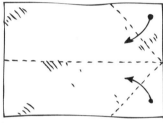

1 FOLD YER PAPER IN HALF THEN OPEN IT. FOLD THE TOP CORNERS DOON TO TAE THE LINE THE MIDDLE FOLD CREATED.

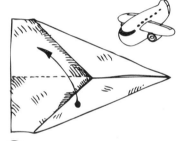

2 FOLD THE TOP CORNER IN HALF AND TOWARDS THE MIDDLE AGAIN.

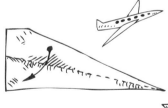

3 FOLD THE PLANE IN HALF, SO THE TRIANGLES ARE ON THE INSIDE. THEN FOLD DOWNWARDS TAE MEET THE MIDDLE FOLD.

4 FOLD THE WINGS UP AGAIN AND THEN YE'RE DONE. GRAB THE MIDDLE SECTION O' THE PLANE AN' GIVE IT A THROW!

A Family Recipe Tae Bring A'body Together

SHORTBREAD

Ingredients:

100g butter

60g caster sugar

150g plain flour

60g milk chocolate

Method:

1. Heat yer oven tae 190c.
2. Put butter and sugar intae a large mixing bowl an' beat together wi' a wooden spoon.
3. Noo mix in the flour till it's a' smooth.
4. Sprinkle flour o'er yer bunker top and roll oot the mixture.
5. Cut oot yer shapes (if ye've a person shaped cutter, that'll be braw, if no then jist cut them intae fingers).
6. Move shapes ontae a baking tray, sprinkle on mair caster sugar and chill for 20 minutes.
7. Put the tray intae the oven and bake fir 15-20 minutes, until they're golden-broon and can slide on the tray.
8. Leave to cool.
9. Melt chocolate in a bowl over boiling water.
10. Spoon melted chocolate intae a piping bag and let cool until it's no' too runny.
11. Let the family pipe the chocolate tae decorate their ain shortbread tae look like them!

JUMBLED TABLET RECIPE!

INGREDIENTS:

50g butter (for greasing)
150ml milk
500g sugar
397g condensed milk
2 tsps. vanilla extract

METHOD:

1. (Adverb) _____ grease a deep (noun) _____.
2. Add the milk and sugar to a large cooking pan, and heat on a high heat until the sugar (verb) _____.
3. (Verb) _____ the condensed milk into the mixture, and cook over a low heat (verb) _____ constantly with a (noun) _____, for 20 to 25 (time) _____.
4. When the mixture has (verb)_____ and turned (adjective) _____, add the 2 (measurement) _____ of vanilla extract.
5. Take it off the heat, and stir constantly, for 10-15 minutes, until it thickens and starts to turn brown and sticks to the (noun) _____.
6. (Verb) _____ into the greased tray and leave to (verb) _____ for 15 minutes.
7. Cut into bite-sized pieces and leave to cool for a further 5 to 10 minutes.
8. Eat!

WORD BANK:

Verb: Dissolves, Melts, Explodes, Pour, Stirring, Thickened, Combusts, Cool

Noun: Baking Tray, Chicken, Toaster, Wooden Spoon, Carrot, Wimbledon Cup

Time: Minutes, Years, Weeks, Hours, Millennia,

Measurement: Teaspoons, Gallons, Miles, Pints, Tonnes, Ladles, Kilograms, Hectares,

Adjective: Gorgeous, Golden Brown, Purple, Large, Hairy, Ripe, Dizzy,

Adverb: Liberally, Angrily, Happily, Loudly, Anxiously, Obnoxiously, Timidly.

The Broons Family Facts

LIKE FAITHER, LIKE SON – BOTH GRANPAW AND PAW BROON BELIEVE ONYTHING TASTES BETTER WHEN IT'S COOKED OOTSIDE. IT'S JIST A SHAME IT'S AYE RAININ' IN SCOTLAND.

MAW BROON'S REAL NAME IS MAIGRET, OR MAGGIE, BUT IS AFFECTIONATELY KNOWN BY A'BODY AS MAW.

GRANPAW BROON HAS AYE BEEN A FAVOURITE, BUT HE DIDNAE FULLY APPEAR IN THE STRIPS UNTIL THE 1940S. BEFORE THEN, HE ONLY APPEARED IN PHOTO FRAMES IN THE BACKGROUND.

IN 1937, IT WAS REVEALED THAT GRANPAW'S BIRTHDAY IS ON THE 6TH OF MARCH.

ALL O' THE CHARACTERS GAVE A HELPIN' HAND DURIN' THE SECOND WORLD WAR, BUT NONE MORE SO THAN HEN AND JOE, WHO SERVED IN THE ARMY FRAE 1939 TILL 1945.

MAGGIE BROON IS AYE CHANGIN' - AND NO' JUST HER CLOTHES! EVERY ARTIST HAS DRAWN MAGGIE DIFFERENTLY, MAKIN' HER A GREAT SYMBOL OF FASHION THROUGH THE AGES.

HEN BROON'S FAVOURITE FOOD IS SPAGHETTI, BECAUSE IT'S LONG AN' THIN - JIST LIKE HIM!

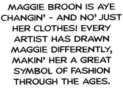

Fun Days Oot

WHETHER IT'S THE SUMMER HOLIDAYS OR JIST A WEEKEND BREAK, IT'S AYE GUID TAE PLAN A FUN DAY OOT FOR THE FAMILY. HERE'S SOME O' OOR FAVOURITES.

WILD WALKS

EASY GOING

● GLENCOE LOCHAN

- A FLAT AND EASY CIRCULAR WALK, BUT WI' THE OPTION TAE GO A BIT FURTHER IF YE LIKE, WI' JOINING WOODLAND TRAILS AN' EVEN A MOUNTAIN PATH. BUT JIST CAUSE IT'S EASY, DISNAE MEAN IT'S NO' REWARDING. THE MIXTURE OF EVERGREENS AND DECIDUOUS TREES MEAN IT'S BRAW LOOKING A' YEAR ROOND.

ADVENTURE EXPLORERS

● BLACK WOOD AND DUN DA-LAMH FORT

- THERE MICHT BE A WEE BIT O' A CLIMB, BUT THE VIEWS ARE WORTH IT AND THERE'S PLENTY TAE EXPLORE ALONG THE WAY, TIRING OOT THE WEE YINS. THE HILLTOP FORT IS JUST THE ICING ON THE CAKE, A'FORE THAT YE'VE GOT A RUINED HOOSE IN THE WOODS, LIKE SOMETHING OOT O' A FAIRY TALE, AN' THERE'S A BRAW PICNIC TABLE AT THE TOP.

BEST BEACHES

● LUSKENTYRE - ISLE OF HARRIS
- A BIT FAR AWA BUT WORTH THE TREK WI' IT'S CARIBBEAN LOOKING WATERS AND SAND. MAYBE SAVE THIS ANE FOR A CAMPING HOLIDAY.

● WEST SANDS - ST. ANDREWS
- GUID FOR ROCK POOLS, SWIMMING AND JIST LOUNGING, THERE'S A REASON THIS BEACH WIS FEATURED IN "CHARIOTS OF FIRE".

● LUCE BAY - DUMFRIES AND GALLOWAY
- ABIDING IN THE WARMEST PART O' THE 'SCOTTISH RIVIERA' AND SWEEPING 20 MILES, THIS BEACH IS PERFECT FOR LOADS O' ACTIVITIES, FROM A BIT O' FITBA TAE SWIMMING. AN' IF THE WEATHER IS AYE CLEAR YE CAN EVEN SEE THE MULL O' GALLOWAY.

COOL CASTLES

● GLAMIS CASTLE
- SUPPOSEDLY HAUNTED BY THE 'MONSTER O' GLAMIS', WI' SECRET ROOMS AN' WINDAES, THERE'S LOADS FOR THE BAIRNS TAE GET EXCITED ABOOT. VERY CENTRAL TO THE WHOLE O' SCOTLAND IT'S EASY TAE GET TAE AND HAS BRAW GROUNDS TAE IF YE FANCY A PICNIC WI' A STUNNING BACKDROP.

● ST. ANDREWS CASTLE
- RIGHT ON THE CLIFFS, ST. ANDREWS CASTLE HAS BRAW VIEWS OWER THE TOON AND NORTH SEA, ESPECIALLY FRAE THE TOWER. BUT IF YE DINNAE LIKE HEIGHTS OR THE WEATHER ISNAE UP TAE MUCH THEN THERE'S THE MINE... BUILT AS A TUNNEL TAE COLLAPSE THE TOWER AN' ENTER THE CASTLE DURING ITS SIEGE IN 1546.

● TANTALLON CASTLE
- SITUATED ON THE CLIFFS OF NORTH BERWICK, THE CASTLE IS SEMI-RUINED, BUT THAT DISNAE SPOIL THE LOOK O' IT. THE CASTLE ALSO OFFERS GUID VIEWS O' THE BASS ROCK AN' A' THE SEABIRDS IT'S FAMOUS FOR.

Broon's Favourite Boogies

CAN YE FIT THESE CLASSIC DANCES TAE THE SQUARES IN THE GRID?

TANGO (5)

CONGA (5)

VELETA (6)

MADISON (7)

MACARENA (8)

CHARLESTON (10)

HOKEY COKEY (10)

GAY GORDONS (10)

VIRGINIA REEL (12)

HIGHLAND FLING (13)

STRIP THE WILLOW (14)

ST. BERNARD'S WALTZ (15)

THE FLYING SCOTSMAN (17)

CANADIAN BARN DANCE (17)

DASHING WHITE SERGEANT (20)

WULLIE'S WAILERS!

WULLIE'S JOKES ARE SO FUNNY YE'LL BE LAUGHIN' YER HEID AFF!

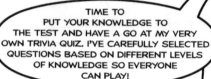

Trivia Time

TIME TO PUT YOUR KNOWLEDGE TO THE TEST AND HAVE A GO AT MY VERY OWN TRIVIA QUIZ. I'VE CAREFULLY SELECTED QUESTIONS BASED ON DIFFERENT LEVELS OF KNOWLEDGE SO EVERYONE CAN PLAY!

FOR THE BAIRNS:

1. IN WHAT COUNTRY WOULD YOU FIND BIG BEN?
2. WHAT IS GLASS MADE OF?
3. WHAT IS A BABY GOAT CALLED?
4. IN DISNEY'S 'THE LITTLE MERMAID' ARIEL HAS TO TRADE WHAT TO RECEIVE LEGS?
5. IN THE BOARD GAME CLUEDO WHAT IS THE NAME OF THE COLONEL?
6. WHICH SOFT DRINK IS OFTEN DESCRIBED AS 'SCOTLAND'S OTHER NATIONAL DRINK'?
7. WHAT IS 0.75 AS THE LOWEST POSSIBLE FRACTION?
8. HOW MANY LEAVES DOES A SHAMROCK HAVE?
9. TRUE OR FALSE: THE SAHARA DESERT IS LARGER THAN AMERICA?
10. IN THE DISNEY FILM 'SNOW WHITE', NAME ALL THE DWARFS?

BIG BAIRN BAMBOOZLES:

1. WHAT IS THE CURRENCY IN JAPAN?
2. WHAT IS THE NAME OF THE ISLAND WHERE NELSON MANDELA WAS IMPRISONED?
3. WHAT SPORT USES THE TERMS TRIPLE SALCHOW AND DOUBLE TOE LOOP?
4. HOW MANY CONTINENTS ARE THERE?
5. WHO WROTE THE NOVEL THE ADVENTURES OF HUCKLEBERRY FINN?
6. WHAT IS THE MOST EXPENSIVE PROPERTY ON THE BRITISH MONOPOLY BOARD?
7. WHAT ARE THE TWO CHEMICAL ELEMENTS THAT MAKE UP WATER?
8. WHICH WELL-LOVED CARTOON ANIMAL MADE HIS DEBUT IN 1940?
9. WHICH KING RULED SCOTLAND FROM 1040 UNTIL 1057?
10. WHAT IS THE MORE USUAL NAME FOR THE POLYGRAPH?

THE GROWN UPS MIGHT GET IT:

1. WHAT IS THE NEXT NUMBER IN THIS SEQUENCE: 5, 11, 23, 47...?

2. WHICH BIRD IS CONSIDERED THE FASTEST IN THE WORLD?

3. WHICH LONDON TUBE LINE IS COLOURED BLACK ON THE UNDERGROUND MAP?

4. WHO WAS THE FIRST SCOTTISH POET LAUREATE?

5. WHO WAS THE FIRST ROMAN EMPEROR TO CONVERT TO CHRISTIANITY?

6. FATS WALLER WAS FAMOUS AS A PLAYER OF WHICH INSTRUMENT?

7. WHO DEFINED DEMOCRACY AS 'GOVERNMENT OF THE PEOPLE, BY THE PEOPLE, FOR THE PEOPLE'?

8. WHICH COUNTRY IS THE HOME OF FETA CHEESE?

9. IN WHICH CITY WILL YOU FIND MICHELANGELO'S FAMOUS 17-FEET-TALL MARBLE SCULPTURE DAVID?

10. BORIS BECKER CONTESTED CONSECUTIVE WIMBLEDON MEN'S SINGLES FINALS IN 1988, 1989, AND 1990, WINNING IN 1989. WHO WAS HIS OPPONENT IN ALL THREE MATCHES?

ONLY HORACE KENS:

1. WHAT IS A GNU?

2. WHAT IS THE LONGEST BONE IN YOUR BODY?

3. IN WHICH COUNTRY IS THE OLDEST UNIVERSITY IN THE WORLD SITUATED?

4. WHICH 1810 POEM BY SIR WALTER SCOTT WAS SET IN THE TROSSACHS REGION OF SCOTLAND?

5. WHICH WELL-KNOWN PAIR LIVE AT 62 WEST WALLABY STREET, WIGAN?

6. HOW MANY APOLLO MISSIONS LANDED MEN ON THE MOON?

7. WHO WAS HENRY VIII'S WIFE AT THE TIME OF HIS DEATH?

8. SUHARTO WAS PRESIDENT OF WHICH LARGE ASIAN NATION?

9. WHICH PHRASE FROM A LATIN POEM BY HORACE IS POPULARLY TRANSLATED AS 'SEIZE THE DAY'?

10. WHAT 1934 FILM WON THE ACADEMY AWARDS FOR BEST PICTURE, DIRECTOR, ACTOR, ACTRESS AND SCREENPLAY?

COMIC CAPERS

OOR WULLIE LOVES TAE READ COMICS, BUT MAYBE THE GOLF COURSE POND ISNAE THE BEST PLACE FOR IT. THERE ARE SIX DIFFERENCES TAE FIND IN THE PICTURES BELOW. CAN YOU SPOT THEM A'?

The Broons Party Games

MUSICAL CHAIRS!

PLACE SOME CHAIRS BACK TAE BACK IN A CIRCLE, IN THE MIDDLE O' THE ROOM. THERE SHOULD BE ONE FEWER THAN THERE ARE PLAYERS. WHILE THE MUSIC IS PLAYIN' A'BODY DANCES CLOCKWISE AROOND THE CHAIRS, THEN WHEN THE MUSIC STOPS AN' YER BAHOOCHIE'S NOT IN A CHAIR - YE'RE OOT!

MURDER IN THE DARK!

SIT IN A CIRCLE ON THE FLOOR. ON A PIECE OF PAPER WRITE 'MURDERER', ON ANOTHER ONE 'DETECTIVE' AND LEAVE THE REST BLANK. THERE SHOULD BE ONE PER PERSON. WHOEVER PICKS DETECTIVE ANNOUNCES THEMSELVES BUT THE MURDERER KEEPS QUIET. WHEN THE LIGHTS GO OOT THE MURDERER TOUCHES THEIR VICTIM, WHO SCREAMS AND LIES DOWN. THE DETECTIVE HAS TAE WORK OOT WHO THE MURDERER IS BUT THEY ONLY HAVE TWO GUESSES!

SCREAM!

THE MESSAGES!

SIT IN A CIRCLE. THE FIRST PERSON SAYS 'I WENT TAE THE SHOP AND BOUGHT...' AND LISTS SOMETHING BEGINNING WI' 'A'. THE NEXT PERSON REPEATS WHAT THE PERSON BEFORE SAID, AND ADDS A NEW ITEM, FOLLOWING THE LETTERS OF THE ALPHABET.

I WENT TAE THE SHOP AND BOUGHT...

Charades

TRY OOT THESE CHARADE PROMPTS FOR BRAW FAMILY FUN! MIND TAE ACT THE TITLES OOT. NAE SPEAKIN' TAE GIVE THE ANSWERS AWA'!

FILMS

FROZEN
HOW TO TRAIN YOUR DRAGON
BRAVEHEART
GREGORY'S GIRL
TRAINSPOTTING
TITANIC

MUSICALS

CATS
HAIRSPRAY
GREASE
FIDDLER ON THE ROOF
THE LION KING
THE PHANTOM OF THE OPERA

BOOKS

THE LORD OF THE RINGS
THE HUNGER GAMES
ANIMAL FARM
LITTLE WOMEN
OF MICE AND MEN
THE WIND IN THE WILLOWS

TELEVISION

PEPPA PIG
DOCTOR WHO
STAR TREK
GAME OF THRONES
CORONATION STREET
STRICTLY COME DANCING

IS IT KING KONG?

I HAVNAE STARTED YET!

The Broons Family Heads!

THE BROONS HAE LOST THEIR HEADS! WHEN YOU SEE THREE OF THE SAME BROONS' HEAD IN A LINE, CROSS THEM OUT. YOU SHOULD BE ABLE TO SPOT 7 LINES!

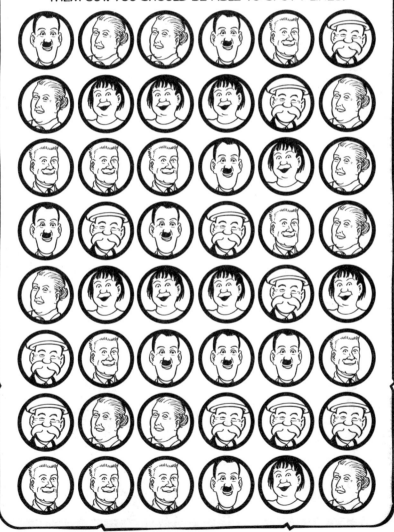

Let's Hae A Party!

US SCOTS KEN HOW TAE THROW A BASH! CAN YE FIND ALL THESE SCOTTISH CELEBRATIONS IN THE WORDSEARCH BELOW?

T	Z	T	H	G	I	N	S	N	R	U	B
C	I	H	O	O	T	E	N	A	X	D	E
E	Y	N	O	S	E	N	A	T	L	Y	L
I	G	D	T	Z	A	J	N	E	S	K	T
L	B	X	A	H	S	Z	E	A	V	J	A
I	Y	U	P	H	E	L	L	Y	A	A	N
D	A	S	H	J	X	P	D	P	E	X	E
H	Y	D	A	L	X	Y	A	P	G	D	S
A	A	B	K	N	L	G	A	R	X	G	D
Y	A	N	A	M	G	O	H	A	K	Y	A
H	O	O	T	E	N	A	N	N	Y	K	Y
S	T	A	N	D	R	E	W	S	D	A	Y

CEILIDH   HOOTENANNY   ST. ANDREW'S DAY

BURNS NIGHT   UP HELLY AA   BELTANE'S DAY

HOGMANAY   T IN THE PARK

Tales From PC MURdOCh's POLiS BOOK

PEOPLE MAY THINK THAT BEING A POLIS OFFICER IN AUCHENSHOOGLE IS AYE EASY - BUT THEY DINNAE KEN ABOOT A' THE MISCHIEF THE RESIDENTS GET UPTAE...

INCIDENT REPORT:
NAME: WILLIAM (WULLIE)
DATE OF INCIDENT: CRIVVENS! EVERY DAY!
CRIME:
● KNOCKING A POLISMAN'S HAT AFF WI' HIS CATTY.
● PUTTING A PUDDOCK IN A POLISMAN'S HAT WI' THE INTENTION FOR HIM TAE PUT IT ON.
● KNOCKING AFF A POLISMAN'S HAT - THIS TIME WI' A SNOWBA'.
● DRIVING HIS CARTIE IN A PEDESTRIAN ZONE.
● DRVING HIS CARTIE OWER THE SERGEANT'S ALREADY SARE FEET!

US SCOTS ARE FAMOUS FOR OUR GUID TASTE IN FOOD AND "NATIONAL DELICACIES"! HERE'S A LIST O' SOME O' OUR FAVOURITES, BUT CAN YE HELP US FIT THE WORDS DOON THE BOTTOM INTAE THIS GRID?

CLOOTIE DUMPLING (15)
ARBROATH SMOKIE (14)
RUMBLEDETHUMPS (14)
BLACK PUDDING (12)
LORNE SAUSAGE (12)
POTATO SCONE (11)
COCK A LEEKIE (11)
CULLEN SKINK (11)

SHORTBREAD (10)
SOOR PLOOM (9)
SCOTCH EGG (9)
CRANACHAN (9)
CLAPSHOT (8)
PORRIDGE (8)
STOVIES (7)
CROWDIE (7)

BANNOCK (7)
OATCAKE (7)
SKIRLIE (7)
TATTIES (7)
TABLET (6)
HAGGIS (6)
MINCE (5)
NEEPS (5)

Broon's Brain-bogglers!

ANSWER THESE BROONS QUESTIONS, THEN UNSCRAMBLE THE HIGHLIGHTED LETTERS TAE WORK OUT WHAT THE ANSWER IS!

ANSWER

--- --- --- --- --- --- --- --- --- ---

I. THE MOST STYLISH OF THE BUNCH! (6)

2. TWA WEE MISCHIEF MAKERS! (3,5)

3. NO CAKE FOR THIS BROON LASS! (6)

4. THIS BROON IS A BIT O' A LADY'S MAN! (3)

5. THE MOUSTACHIOED MAN OF THE HOOSE! (3,5)

6. HEN BROON'S FAVOURITE PIECE O' CLOTHING! (4,4)

7. THE SMART ONE IN THE FAMILY! (6)

8. THE BEST COOK IN THE BROONS FAMILY! (3,5)

9. HE'S AWA' AT THE ALLOTMENT! (7)

IO. SHE'S A MINI MAW! (3,5)

II. THE NAME OF THE BROON'S STREET! (5,6)

TONI'S EXTRA SPECIAL HAGGIS CARBONARA!

I MAY LIVE IN SCOTLAND, BUT MY GREAT, GREAT GRANPAPPY CAME FRAE ITALY! THAT MEANS MOST-A-ME FOOD IS A MIXTURE OF CLASSIC ITALIANO AND SCOTTISH, JIST LIKE THIS HAGGIS CARBONARA RECIPE!

SERVES 8

INGREDIENTS:

100G UNSALTED BUTTER
HAGGIS (750G)
2 WHITE ONIONS, SLICED
3 GARLIC CLOVES, CRUSHED
100G PARMESAN
200G CHESTNUT MUSHROOMS, SLICED
200ML DOUBLE CREAM
800G OF PASTA - IDEALLY SPAGHETTI OR LINGUINI
1 TBS OLIVE OIL
SALT AND GROUND BLACK PEPPER TAE TASTE

HOW TAE DO IT:

1. HALF FILL AS LARGE A PAN AS POSSIBLE WITH WATER AND PUT OVER A HIGH HEAT.

2. ADD SALT AND THE OLIVE OIL (THIS STOPS THE PASTA FROM STICKING) TO THE WATER, AND ONCE BOILING ADD THE PASTA. IF YOU WANT YOUR SPAGHETTI 'AL DENTE' TAKE A STRAND OUT OF THE WATER 1-2 MINS BEFORE THE END OF THE COOKING TIME AND BITE INTO IT, THERE SHOULD BE A SMALL WHITE DOT IN THE CENTRE O' THE SPAGHETTI.

3. MEANWHILE, PUT THE BUTTER INTAE A LARGE FRYING PAN OWER A MEDIUM HEAT AND FRY THE HAGGIS, ONION AND GARLIC AND STIR CONTINUOUSLY.

4. WHEN THE ONION IS SOFT AND BEGINS TO COLOUR, ADD THE MUSHROOMS.

5. ONCE THE MUSHROOMS ARE SOFT AND COOKED THROUGH, ADD THE CREAM, 3/4 OF THE CHEESE AND THE SALT AND PEPPER TO TASTE.

6. ONCE THE CREAM IS HEATED THROUGH AND JUST STARTING TO BUBBLE (THIS SHOULD TAKE ABOUT 2-3 MINUTES) TAKE OFF THE HEAT.

7. MEANWHILE, ONCE YOUR PASTA IS COOKED, DRAIN THE WATER OVER THE SINK AND LEAVE TO STEAM FOR A MINUTE TO EVAPORATE THE EXCESS WATER.

8. NOW, USING TONGS, ADD THE PASTA TO THE SAUCE AND MIX THOROUGHLY.

9. DISH UP THE PASTA AND SAUCE INTO BOWLS AND SPRINKLE OVER THE REMAINING CHEESE AND MORE GROUND BLACK PEPPER ON TOP.

93

Like Clockwork!

GRANPAW AND PAW BROON ARE TOO CHEAP TAE TAK' THE CUCKOO
CLOCK TAE GET FIXED SO THEY'RE HAVIN' A GO THEMSELVES...

...BUT THEY KEEP LOSING ALL THE PARTS! CAN YOU CLOCK TWENTY
DIFFERENCES IN THE PICTURES ABOVE?

PLAYIN' GAMES AN' FAMILY
ACTIVITIES DISNAE ALWAYS END
AS PLANNED IN GLEBE STREET.
BE SURE TAE STICK TAE THE
RULES AN' AVOID CHEATIN' BY
IGNORIN' THE ANSWER PAGES
TILL YE'RE READY.

PAGE 3) CROSSED THREADS
THREAD A

PAGE 7) GONE FISHIN'

PAGE 9) CROSSED LINES
LINE B

PAGE 12) CRACK THE CODE
1)   THESE TIN CANS ARE RARE!
2)   AYE, AN' NAE ONE KENS WHIT WE'RE SAYING!
3)   DAE YE THINK WE NEED THE CANS AN' THE CODE?
4)   YE CAN NEVER BE TOO CAREFUL!

PAGE 13) TANGLE TEASER
BOAB AND SOAPY
ECK AND WULLIE

PAGE 20) HORACE BROON'S SUDOKU

EASY

5	3	4	7	8	6	1	9	2
6	1	9	4	2	3	8	5	7
2	8	7	1	5	9	6	3	4
7	4	1	5	6	2	9	8	3
8	5	2	3	9	7	4	1	6
3	9	6	8	1	4	2	7	5
1	2	5	6	7	8	3	4	9
4	6	8	9	3	5	7	2	1
9	7	3	2	4	1	5	6	8

HARD

1	9	4	7	6	5	8	2	3
7	5	3	2	8	4	1	9	6
6	2	8	3	9	1	7	5	4
9	7	1	6	5	8	4	3	2
3	8	6	4	7	2	5	1	9
5	4	2	1	3	9	6	8	7
4	1	5	9	2	7	3	6	8
2	6	7	8	1	3	9	4	5
8	3	9	5	4	6	2	7	1

PAGE 22) PRIMROSE'S PUZZLERS

EASY PEASY:

I. PLUTO,   2. 52,   3. GLASS SLIPPER,   4. AFRICA,   5. ED SHEERAN,   6. S,
7. MARS,   8. FISH,   9. LOCH,   IO. ZOOTOPIA

WILLIAM MIGHT KNOW:

I. GLASGOW,   2. KILIMANJARO,   3. BLUE, YELLOW, BLACK, GREEN, RED,
4. THE PACIFIC,   5. 4   6. SCOTLAND,   7. MARIO,   8. THE AMAZON,   9. GOLD,   IO. 64

HEAD SCRATCHERS:

I. QUEBEC,   2. THE NORTHERN LIGHTS,   3. MICHELANGELO,
4. THEODORE ROOSEVELT,   5. R.E.M.,   6. CULZEAN CASTLE, AYRSHIRE,
7. KITTENS,   8. HAMLET,   9. H2O,   IO. LIMA

PRIMROSE LEVEL SMARTIE-PANTS:

I. A SCOTTISH COIN OF LOW VALUE,   2. DUCK,   3. J.D. SALINGER,
4. HMY BRITANNIA,   5. I876,   6. INSECTS,   7. BILL (WILLIAM) CLINTON,
8. OCEAN DEPTH,   9. ZINC,   IO. AN OTTER

PAGE 25) CRACK THE CODE

MAW'S HIDDEN THE GUID SWEETIES INSIDE THE BREAD BIN.

PAGE 26) HORACE'S SUPER SCIENCE WORD SEARCH

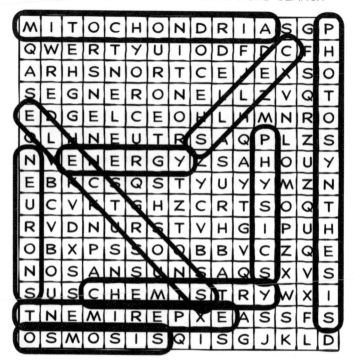

PACE 27) MAKE THE GRADE

PAGE 36) WORD JUMBLES

LANKY
PLUMP
BOOKISH
BOXER
MISCHIEVOUS
WEE LAMB
RAMBUNCTIOUS
GLAMOUROUS

PAGE 37) DAPHNE PUZZLE

PAGE 41) ON THE RUN

PATH C

PAGE 48) SILLY SOOKERS

PAGE 49) BONNY SCOTLAND
ACROSS

2. HEATHER, 3. LOCH, 5. EDINBURGH, 7. PUDDOCKS, 8. STOORIE BURN,
10. GRUMPY GREENS, 11. RIVER TAY, 12. PORRIDGE
DOWN
1. BEN NEVIS, 4. HIGHLAND COWS, 6. STOORIE BRAE, 9. MUNRO

PAGE 56) I KEN WHAT I KEN
1. C, 2. B, 3. B, 4. A, 5. C, 6. C

PAGE 57) MATCH THE WORD TAE THE IMAGE
5 BREEKS, 5 BAHOOCHIES, 1 BUNNET, 8 DRAMS, 1 HAGGIS, 11 LUGS,
11 NEBS, 15 OXTERS.

PAGE 59) WELCOME TO 10 GLEBE STREET
ACROSS

3. LUM, 5. DAPHNE, 6. DOLLY, 7. HEN, 8. CLOOTIE DUMPLING, 9. MAW
BROON, 11. TEN, 12. DINNERTIME.
DOWN
1. AUCHENTOGLE, 2. MAGGIE, 4. ALLOTMENT, 10. JOE.

PAGE 61) WORD JUMBLES!
CRICKET, ROUNDERS, FITBA, CARTIE, TENNIS, CATAPULT, BUCKET

PAGE 70) MAW BROON'S CRAFTY WORD SEARCH

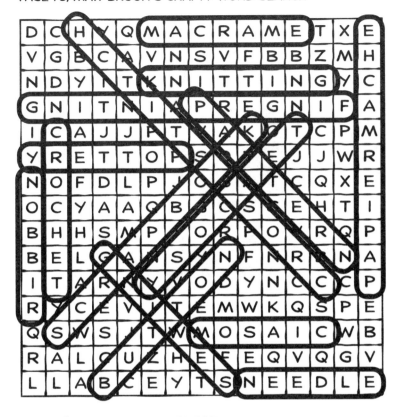

PAGE 73) JUMBLED TABLET RECIPE

1. LIBERALLY GREASE A DEEP BAKING TRAY.
2. ADD THE MILK AND SUGAR TO A LARGE COOKING PAN, AND HEAT ON A HIGH HEAT UNTIL THE SUGAR DISSOLVES.
3. POUR THE CONDENSED MILK INTO THE MIXTURE, AND COOK OVER A LOW HEAT, STIRRING CONSTANTLY WITH A WOODEN SPOON FOR 20 TO 25 MINUTES.
4. WHEN THE MIXTURE HAS THICKENED AND TURNED GOLDEN BROWN, ADD THE 2 TEASPOONS OF VANILLA EXTRACT.
5. TAKE IT OFF THE HEAT, AND STIR CONSTANTLY, FOR 10-15 MINUTES, UNTIL IT THICKENS AND STARTS TO TURN BROWN AND STICKS TO THE WOODEN SPOON.
6. POUR INTO THE GREASED TRAY AND LEAVE TO COOL FOR 15 MINUTES.
7. CUT INTO BITE-SIZED PIECES AND LEAVE TO COOL FOR A FURTHER 5 TO 10 MINUTES.
8. EAT!

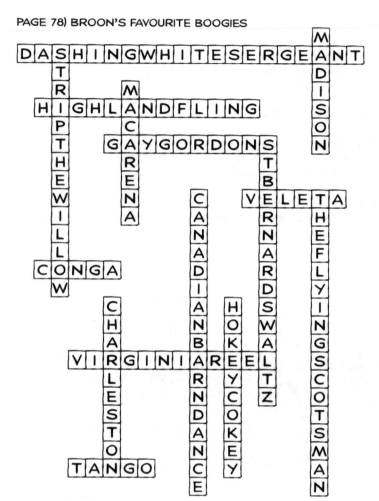

PAGE 80) TRIVIA TIME

SOME FIR THE BAIRNS:
I. ENGLAND, 2. SAND, 3. A KID, 4. HER VOICE, 5. MUSTARD, 6. IRN BRU, 7. 3/4, 8. 3, 9. TRUE, IO. DOC, GRUMPY, HAPPY, SLEEPY, BASHFUL, SNEEZY AND DOPEY.

BIG BAIRN BAMBOOZLES:
I. YEN, 2. ROBBEN ISLAND, 3. FIGURE SKATING, 4. 7, 5. MARK TWAIN, 6. MAYFAIR, 7. HYDROGEN AND OXYGEN, 8. BUGS BUNNY, 9. MACBETH, IO. LIE DETECTOR.

THE GROWN UPS MIGHT GET IT:

I. 95, 2. PEREGRINE FALCON , 3. NORTHERN, 4. EDWIN MORGAN,
5. CONSTANTINE, 6. PIANO, 7. ABRAHAM LINCOLN, 8. GREECE, 9. FLORENCE,
IO. STEFAN EDBERG.

ONLY HORACE KENS:

I. WILDEBEEST, 2. FEMUR, 3. MOROCCO, 4. 'THE LADY OF THE LAKE'
5. WALLACE AND GROMIT, 6. 6, 7. CATHERINE PARR, 8. INDONESIA, 9. CARPE
DIEM, IO. IT HAPPENED ONE NIGHT.

PAGE 82) COMIC CAPERS

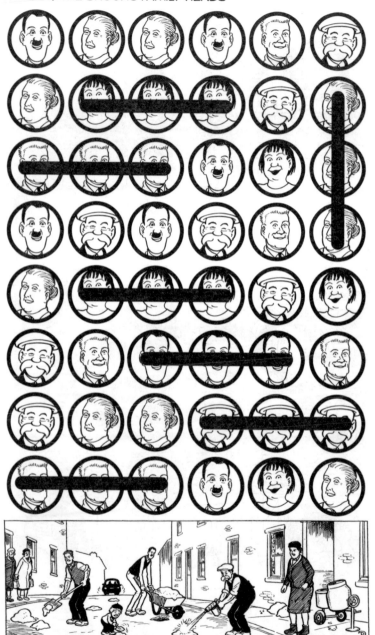

ANSWER

AUCHENTOGLE

PAGE 93) SPAGHETTI SOOKERS
PLATE A

PAGE 94) LIKE CLOCKWORK!